The London Hospital Illustrated
250 Years

The London Hospital Illustrated
250 Years

250 Years

B.T. BATSFORD LTD · LONDON

© The London Hospital 1990
Editor for The London Hospital: Claire Daunton

Designer: Alan Hamp

First published 1990

ISBN 0 7134 6491 7

Typeset in Monophoto Sabon by Servis Filmsetting Ltd,
Manchester
Printed in Great Britain by The Bath Press, Bath
for the Publisher
B.T. Batsford Ltd
4 Fitzhardinge Street, London W1H 0AH

Contents

HUMANI NIHIL A ME ALIENUM PUTO

Preface

This book has been compiled with two purposes in mind – to celebrate and to commemorate. It is intended to celebrate 250 years of The London Hospital by telling the story of the hospital and illustrating many aspects of its work. It is also intended to commemorate all the staff who have worked for the hospital, the patients who have benefited from it and others who have supported it with their time and money. It is hoped, in addition, that the book, by reflecting on our history, will help us to move forward into the future with confidence.

A number of people, both present and former staff of The London Hospital, have been involved in the compiling of this book. They represent different professions and occupations within the hospital and have tried to reflect as many aspects as possible of the life and work of the institution. Their names are given here in alphabetical order: John Blandy, Pat Burgess, Claire Daunton, Grace Dedman, Bob Fewell, Phyllis Friend, Denis Gibbs, Joan Hinds, Maureen Scholes.

There are too many individuals and departments involved in the story of The London to mention all those who helped. Special thanks, however, must go to Miss Margaret Broadley, Mrs Theresa Clark, Mrs Peggy Crispin and Professor Francis Fish. Thanks are also due to The Special Trustees of The London Hospital and to Mr Timothy Auger of Batsford for bringing this project to a successful conclusion.

The aim of the contributors has been to include as many facets as possible of the life and work of the hospital over two-and-a-half centuries. No history is ever complete and some references will have been omitted, but we hope the book tells The London's story in an enjoyable and informative way.

Knutsford

Introduction

I · From Infirmary to Hospital: 1740–1854

In 1740 the War of Jenkins' Ear between England and Spain was being fought. George II was King and Robert Walpole was Prime Minister. But for the people of the East End of London, 1740 was more notable for the troubles it brought – a severe winter, a bad harvest, and the ever-present threat of disease. It was in this atmosphere of gloom that seven men – friends and professional associates – talked together of starting an infirmary for the sick and poor to be situated to the east of the City of London.

This type of venture was not unique at the time. The Westminster, Guy's, St George's and the Middlesex hospitals were all founded in the early years of the eighteenth century. Their common aim was to provide better care for the sick in growing urban areas. Some were religious foundations but others were founded by professional medical men in association with philanthropists and businessmen, with the patronage of members of the nobility being sought to lend distinction to the ventures.

The London was no exception in the manner of its birth. It was founded at a meeting in the Feathers Tavern, Cheapside, by a group of seven men – John Harrison, a surgeon, Josiah Cole, an apothecary, Fotherley Baker, a lawyer, and their associates. There was a difference, however, in that The London specifically addressed itself to the sick poor amongst the 'merchant seamen and manufacturing classes', and therefore by definition at that time, to the East End community. It has never departed from its tradition of service to the local community despite its becoming a large teaching hospital with a national and international reputation.

John Harrison was the leading member of the group and it was he who purchased the house in Featherstone Street (close to City Road), the first site of the London Infirmary.

A physician, a surgeon, an apothecary and a married couple as porter and housekeeper were appointed, the house was fitted out and furnished, and £20 was set aside for the first year's running costs. The infirmary opened on 3 November 1740.

The task of raising the money to finance the venture, however, was not an easy one. Indeed the business of fund-raising was to become a common thread throughout the history of The London – something to which much effort and ingenuity would be devoted. In 1740 two thousand letters were sent out to ask people to subscribe five guineas a year for the upkeep of the infirmary and its patients. In return for their five guineas, subscribers would become governors of the infirmary and have a say in its running; they would also be counted amongst an ever-growing group of the middle class who saw such ventures as a mark of respectability. The fact that the Duke of Richmond became a subscriber made this an even more attractive proposition; but, in spite of that, not many responded. In fact the opening of the infirmary in November 1740 was something of an act of blind faith as there was only one shilling in the bank at that time.

Before long, however, subscriptions began to come in and it was necessary to choose a small group from amongst the whole body of subscribers to attend to the daily business. Whilst everyone could attend occasional meetings held in a tavern, only the small chosen group were eligible to meet once a week at the infirmary where they supervised its management and finance. At the same time as this group was established, other, far-reaching decisions regarding the policy of the infirmary were taken. Most notable amongst these was that the subscribers alone should have the right to recommend patients. This rule which gave subscribers great powers of local patronage remained in force until the end of the nineteenth century. It was not long, too, before further refinements were added to the post of governor. Those who contributed five guineas a year were governors; those who contributed a lump sum of thirty guineas became life governors. Local traders soon realized the value of having the right to nominate patients for treatment, and it became necessary to limit the right of governors to only one patient at a time.

By now the infirmary had been forced by increasing numbers to move to larger premises in Prescot Street, between the Tower and Aldgate. At that time it was an area of theatres and other 'places of entertainment' and not wholly respectable. The infirmary was there to serve the local community and the sick poor of the locality; they were finding it increasingly difficult to obtain treatment as many of them could not get the letter from a governor which would qualify them. It was then that the system of paying a penny to be allowed to petition for treatment was introduced.

Despite this increase in numbers of governors and patients, the infirmary was not secure financially. This was evident from the financial statement made to the first formal meeting of the Court of Governors in the Haberdashers' Hall in May 1742, which was chaired by the Duke of Richmond. Out of a sum of £640 saved, only £57 was left. It was then that a novel way of maintaining the fund-raising impetus was devised. John Harrison suggested that an Anniversary Feast should be held each year – that there should be a sermon followed by a dinner with entertainment, at which a collection should be made for the infirmary. The suggestion was taken up and indeed was followed for many years to great effect. It became a great public event, with a procession, liveried attendants and many spectators. It also became an occasion to dispense subscription forms and to publish an annual report and set of accounts.

Life inside the infirmary, however, was not entirely satisfactory. Though the medical needs were not badly attended to by the standards of the time – one physician and one surgeon plus an apothecary to about 30 in-patients and any number of out-patients – the management of the institution and the physical care of the patients were criticized. The governors were anxious to avoid the problems they had encountered with the first matron, who had been discharged for misconduct, and eventually appointed Mrs Elizabeth Broad who retained her appointment for 15 years. Those hired as nurses, maids and housekeepers were generally without any education and training and they were left to deal with the patients unsupervised. The infirmary was

not well provided with water and often the bed-clothes, the patients' clothes and the building itself were left dirty and unkempt. Neither was the area around the building a salubrious one. Infections were rife – the infirmary tried to exclude patients with chronic disorders, and those unlikely to benefit from admission were discouraged. The hospital concentrated on certain conditions and excluded others, as was the practice in the other hospitals founded at that time.

The surgeons and physicians who served there began to train pupils by taking them into the infirmary and discussing with them the patients' illnesses and by allowing them, on occasions, to administer treatment. This method of teaching was combined with lectures and anatomy classes which were taken outside the infirmary: The London was among the first to train pupils (students) in a way that was more than a mere apprenticeship.

It is clear, however, from the records of the infirmary – or hospital as it was coming to be called – that the professional medical men were controlled by the governors. The governors, those who paid their subscriptions and raised funds, were the ones who made the rules not only for the running of the house but also for the conduct of patients and staff. The rules were many and strict, and those who sat on the committees seem to have been able and dedicated men, though little is known of them as individuals.

Their dedication and common sense showed itself to be most in evidence in the choice of the site for a new building, something that became a pressing need as the 1740s wore on, with the increase in the number of patients and the deterioration of the Prescot Street buildings. In fact the decision to have purpose-built premises and the manner of choosing the site were handled with great competence. The governors appointed a committee under the Earl of Macclesfield to be responsible for this task and requested that the committee should act with speed. The committee appointed a surveyor, Mainwaring, and set him to work immediately to locate a suitable site for building. Despite the need for speed, however, it was not until almost two years later that Whitechapel –

and more precisely the Mount and Mount Field – were chosen.

The area was then in the midst of agricultural land with the villages of Bethnal Green and Mile End to the north and east, and the river and docks to the south. It was, however, a well-known area through which passed the main road from Essex into the City of London. The land was owned by the City Corporation and leased by them to several people. The process of obtaining the land from the lessees and the City Corporation was a tortuous one but it was done, at a cost of more than £2000, and building began in 1752.

The commencement of Mainwaring's building attracted much attention and The London Hospital, as it was now universally known, became a fashion-

able topic. The process of building the new hospital, however, was beset with difficulties; there were problems with workmen and with thieves, there were disputes about the proximity of the building to the road out to Essex, and there was the constant need to raise enough money to keep up with building costs.

It was not until 1759, seven years after the foundation stone had been laid, that the building was finished; and even then it was not the whole building as Mainwaring had planned it, but only the central block.

The building that was partially opened in 1757 had been built solely from public subscriptions. The sum of £18,000 had been raised by various means and the manner of its raising had put The London

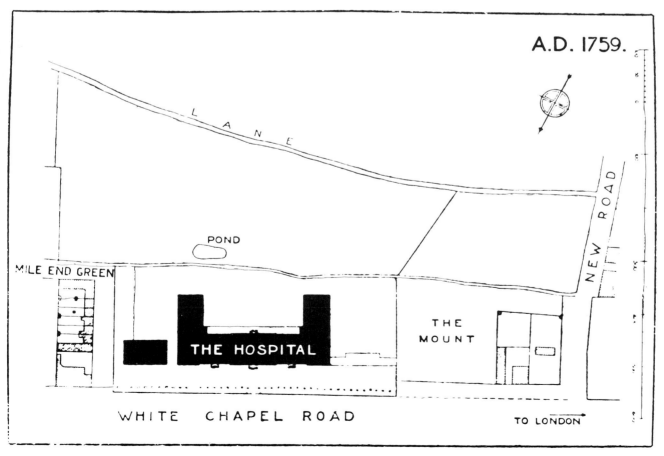

very much in the public eye. It was unfortunate that many of those who had been involved in the founding of the infirmary in Prescot Street were not alive to witness the opening of The London Hospital in Whitechapel.

We know from William Bellers' painting of the hospital at this time (though it does admit of some artistic licence) and from contemporary maps, that the area was semi-rural. What the maps and painting do not indicate is that the area was becoming more populated and more heavily industrialized.

Immigrants had always settled in the area to the east of the City, in the vicinity of the docks. There had been Sephardic Jews, Flemings and Huguenots coming in the sixteenth and seventeenth centuries, but in small enough numbers to be absorbed well into the community. It was not until the mid-eighteenth century that an influx of English weavers into the traditionally foreign quarter of Spitalfields and a steadily increasing number of Irish immigrants coming into the Shoreditch area presented problems. The pressure of increased numbers and consequent difficulties in finding work led to riots in 1736 in Shoreditch and 1769 in Spitalfields. The London, then, was situated in an area where immigration accounted for a growing population; and this was a factor that was to become ever more important in the area, and to the life of the hospital.

The attention devoted by the committee to the erection of the new building in Whitechapel, and to the establishment of The London Hospital as a well-known institution, gave way in the 1760s to a period of internal reform and improvements. A system of house visitors was introduced; these were to make regular inspections of the hospital. Their reports indicate that they were concerned mainly with two issues – the daily management of the hospital, and the religious element in this daily routine.

It must be noted that The London was not founded as a religious institution – unlike several other eighteenth-century medical foundations. Although it had links with the Anglican church from the beginning, it was not an Anglican foundation. This was something that surfaced again and again over the centuries as the ebb and flow of immigrants with different nationalities and different creeds continued. In the latter part of the eighteenth century, however, attempts were made to tie the running of The London more closely to Anglican practices. The house committee, prompted by reports of house visitors, tried to insist that all staff should attend chapel daily and that patients should have regular visits from the chaplain.

One of those most anxious to see the spiritual life of the hospital improved was William Blizard, a young surgeon, who had trained as a dressing pupil at The London under Henry Thompson (who had replaced John Harrison) and was taken on to the staff in 1780. Blizard was to have a profound influence on the hospital and on the teaching of medicine. He was also instrumental in founding the Samaritan Society to give practical help to poor patients, and in founding the medical club which brought together both past and present pupils and teaching staff of the medical college. Both societies continue to flourish today.

The docks meanwhile began to develop into a large industry and in turn fostered the establishment of services and industries connected with a growing port – including ironworks, lumber yards, mills, rope-making, brewing, and ship-building. They also brought problems of a rising population, rising land and house prices and an increase in the demand for space in the hospital. The house committee responded in two ways: it began to build and to extend, and it began to sublease some of the land surrounding the Whitechapel site which it had on a long lease from the Corporation of London. It also bought land adjoining the hospital which gave it room to expand and made it rich in terms of property. The estate now amounted to 20 acres, an important factor in future planning and development. Two new wings were started to complete Mainwaring's original design and by 1778 both were finished – again through subscriptions alone.

The hospital then entered the last decades of the eighteenth century in a confident mood. It was with this confidence that William Blizard, now a member of staff of the hospital and a surgeon of repute, pressed his idea for a medical school attached to The London. He believed that teaching and medical science could not advance unless the theory and practice of medicine were combined with lectures on anatomy and dissection, and experimentation. The governors were both suspicious and afraid of this new concept. Though they were willing to lease land to Blizard they considered that the medical college should be separate from the hospital. Blizard persisted. Raising money by appeal and publicity, and contributing from his limited private income, he soon found sufficient funds to erect a small building next to the hospital which opened as a medical school in October 1785.

Suspicion of the enterprise was not the only reason for the governors' unwillingness to support Blizard. The hospital itself was going through a financial crisis arising partly from national economic difficulties as a consequence of the American War of Independence, and partly from overspending on the part of the governors. The realization of the seriousness of the situation, however, galvanized the governors into drastic action; wards were closed, staff were pensioned off, economies were made in the running of the hospital. All this, of course, was not without cost to the patients in terms of availability of treatments and the upkeep of the wards.

Other London hospitals seem to have weathered the economic storm mainly because they charged for food, for the nurses and for certain items. There was a whole series of visits to the hospital by governors and by outsiders seeking first-hand information on the situation to see what they could do to improve matters. Recommendations were made for improving cleanliness and the state of the building and for changing the diet; but the underlying situation did not get much better. The governors were still short of money, subscriptions were not worth what they had been 20 years before, and the crisis of the American War had been replaced by that of the French Revolutionary War.

This period of economic crisis occurred just as the impact of increasing industrialization began to be felt with some force in London, and particularly in the East End. The wars and the growth of the East India Company's overseas trade also had made for a large increase in the ship-building industry. This in turn drew other industries to the area around the docks and attracted large numbers of immigrants to London both from other parts of Britain (especially Ireland) and from overseas. Yet at a time of increasing activity in the East End and an increasing population, The London Hospital still had closed wards and a depleted staff and was not able to extricate itself from its difficulties. William Blizard, for all his influence over the pupils and reputation as a surgeon, was not able to solve the underlying problems of the hospital – poor management and poor husbanding of financial resources.

Disagreements over the running of the hospital between the governors and the professional staff, and a growing economic crisis, left The London in a sorry state as the eighteenth century drew to a close.

The years following the end of the French Revolutionary and Napoleonic Wars were difficult ones for the country and the consequences of war were compounded by poor harvests and economic difficulties. Many who had come into the East End to work in the dockyards and associated industries when business had been booming now found themselves in great poverty. The pressure of expansion had resulted in large numbers of people needing to be housed and fed and had consequently meant the development of the Whitechapel area. The hospital found itself being closed in. It was at this point that the governors decided to build another wing. By the end of the 1830s The London had another six wards in operation.

Between 1801 and 1831 the population of the area almost doubled, mainly the result of the influx of immigrants from Ireland and continental Europe displaced by hunger and war. There was also an increase in the number of Jews coming into the area (though the main wave of Jewish immigration which was to have most effect on The London did not take place until the end of the nineteenth century) and this had a direct effect upon the hospital. In 1836 the house committee agreed that Jews should have separate facilities for food and washing. This respect for minority creeds and faiths became a characteristic of The London; Catholics, Anglicans, Jews and Non-Conformists and, latterly, Muslims have all benefited from it. Nor was the charity all one way. While The London was respectful of all religions, it also benefited from legacies and donations from Jews, Quakers and Unitarians as well as Anglicans; from people such as the Rothschilds, Raphaels and Samuels on the one hand, and the Gurneys, Buxtons and Hanburys on the other.

The area developed as the ship-building trade changed with the introduction of iron vessels and as London became an important trading port. At the same time as other industries grew up around the port, there was a consequent risk of disease, injury and death. The growth in the population, and the parallel growth of hospital and medical school gave greater scope for the development of medical studies.

During the early years of the hospital, students had been tolerated on the wards, but by the middle of the nineteenth century they were becoming indispensable for coping with the increase in patients. This was true throughout London and new medical schools were opened attached to The Middlesex Hospital, University College Hospital and Charing Cross Hospital. In addition, courses were tightened up, examinations became more formal and the system of a total fee for all training was introduced.

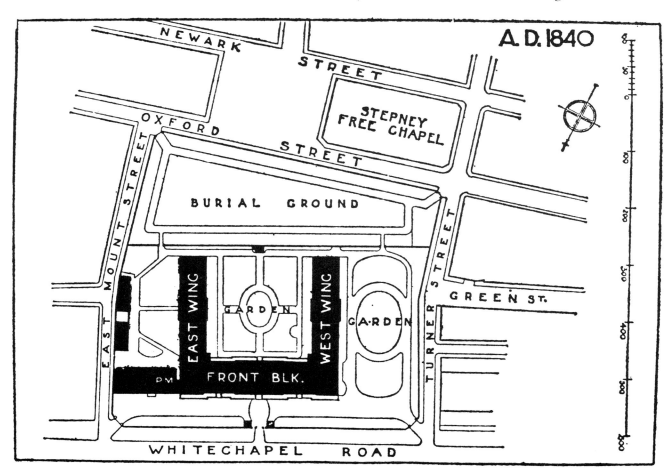

The London Hospital Medical College was already attracting pupils from far and wide on account of the number and range of cases that they could study. They were required to live close to the hospital so that they could be called at short notice and in the medical wards in particular they carried much of the responsibility for caring for the patients.

The relationship between college and hospital was recognized formally by the hospital in 1837 but it was declared that the college had no call on the general funds of the hospital or on the land on which the college stood. By the middle years of the century, however, the house committee recognized the importance of the college and the provision of good facilities and agreed to fund a new building. This consisted of two large lecture theatres, two museums, a library, a dissecting room and two smaller lecture rooms and was opened in 1854.

II · The London Makes its Mark: 1855–1918

The middle years of the nineteenth century were a time when cholera was rampant throughout many areas of the East End. This was mainly due to poor sanitation and housing and to the lack of an adequate fresh water supply. The worst years were 1831, 1848, 1855 and 1866. Initially The London refused to accept cholera patients because of the effect they would have on the work of the hospital as a whole. This refusal, however, elicited such a hostile reaction from the local community and public opinion in general that special wards had to be opened for cholera victims.

The misery inflicted by these epidemics brought to the attention of the general public the appalling conditions of the East End. In 1847 a Metropolitan Commission of Sewers was established which led to the building of sewers and the erection of three pumping stations. In 1857 Lord Shaftesbury began the first of many attempts to improve housing conditions by introducing a bill to establish control over lodging houses and to introduce schemes for the building of houses for the poor.

The London itself had been at work improving the building and widening the scope of its medical care. One example of this was the attitude to maternity cases. In the early years of the hospital, pregnant women were turned away and sent to a 'lying in hospital'; but by the middle of the nineteenth century there was an obstetrician on the staff of The London and a clinic for women of the area. Anaesthetics, dentistry and ophthalmology were gradually intro-duced during these years. Unfortunately, the increase in the range of medical care was not always matched by accommodation or quality of nursing.

In 1862 a special committee was established to look at the problem of overcrowding in the hospital. It had no hesitation in recommending the building of an additional wing, which was to be called the Alexandra Wing, after the Princess of Wales, later Queen Alexandra. The Alexandra Wing came into service almost before it was completed in 1866 to care for the victims of the last great cholera epidemic. The hospital was required to mobilize itself for a very serious situation and this time governors responded with a positive attitude – visiting the hospital and allowing for the hiring of more nurses to cope with the great increase in disease and death.

The cholera epidemic of 1866 showed well the deficiencies in the nursing care that the hospital was able to give. The standard of nursing at The London at this time was no better and no worse than in many other similar institutions and probably would have gone on in much the same way – i.e. with poorly trained, badly disciplined, illiterate nurses offering sympathy but little else – if the climate of opinion towards nursing had not started to change. Florence Nightingale had set up her training school at St Thomas's and had drawn to the attention of the public, through the school and through her work in the Crimean War, the necessity of establishing a nursing profession. In 1867 one of the Nightingale trainees, Miss Swift, came to The London to take up the post of matron and she was responsible for introducing the governors to the idea of a nurse training school. This was started in 1870 and in 1873 it was decided to build separate accommodation to house a school for nurses.

The building of the Alexandra Wing had enabled the hospital to enlarge the area for receiving and treating casualties. It had enabled it to establish other new departments in line with the increasing specialization of medicine and surgery. Departments such as morbid anatomy and pathology and a skin department were able to function separately from the 1870s.

What the new building had not done was enable the hospital to keep pace with the growth in population in the East End, the consequences of poverty and the rise in industrial accidents. The hospital had neither space nor money to cope with the population that had almost doubled again since 1831, so an appeal was launched for money to run the hospital and erect yet another extension to the building. Despite the seemingly impossible target the money was raised and an extension was started in 1874. A large proportion of this money came from the Grocers' Company and the Stock Exchange whose members thereby acquired the important right to nominate patients for admission.

The London, with its Grocers' Wing extension, opened by Queen Victoria in 1876 (a great social occasion and a national as well as a local event) was now a large, complex organization with a growing reputation; and the Queen's visit did much to enhance this. It was attracting medical men who became famous for their work. Among these were Jonathan Hutchinson and Morell Mackenzie – the former a surgeon of world renown and the latter the father and founder of British laryngology: and Hughlings Jackson who established The London as a great centre for the study of neurology. Frederick Treves, a surgeon whose name became known throughout the land, had just graduated from The London and was starting to apply his enormous energy and abilities. The London offered these men and many of their colleagues the facilities and range of work that enabled them to establish themselves as leading members of their profession and to build up well-respected departments.

Many of those who were leaders in their own field of medicine also had teaching and administrative duties in the college. They gave lectures, held tutorials, conducted examinations, sat on committees, appointed students and house officers and liaised with the house committee. All of this was unpaid work; to earn a living they had to travel to other parts of London for private patients. The governing body of the college, the medical council, met frequently and rarely consisted of more than three or four members. It dealt mainly with relations with the hospital and on one occasion in 1867 it had to deal with requests to both bodies from three prospective women students, one of whom was Elizabeth Garrett Anderson. Their request to become students at The London was turned down. In the same year, at a later meeting of the medical council, it was decided to institute the offices of dean and vice-dean and that the dean should be the secretary of the medical council. They were to be responsible for the welfare of the students and for the maintenance of standards throughout the school, as well as for carrying out the decisions of the council. The first two holders of these offices, Jonathan Hutchinson as dean and Walter Rivington as vice-dean, both surgeons, were outstanding in their own fields and made great contributions to medical education. Rivington in his book *The Medical Profession*, published in 1879, proved himself to be a pioneer in the field.

The structured world inhabited by the students and their teachers was in great contrast to the world outside college and hospital. The works of Charles Booth and Henry Mayhew, and the engravings of Gustave Doré, amongst others, give some idea of the kind of world this was, but it is difficult to imagine just how dreadful was life in 'the great wen'. Overcrowding, an insanitary environment, lack of work, appalling working conditions, prostitution and drunkenness, theft and violence all combined to make the area bleak and frightening. The hospital was part of this scene. It trained Dr Barnardo who became world-famous for his work with destitute children and it enabled Frederick Treves to rescue the Elephant Man from a 'peep show' opposite the hospital and offer him a home. It also evoked hostility amongst the local population when it was thought that bodies were being used for dissection and because it was difficult to obtain treatment without a letter of recommendation from a governor.

It was to this large, active and over-stretched institution that two people came towards the end of the century who were to change it dramatically – Eva Lückes, to be matron, and Sydney Holland (later Viscount Knutsford) to be chairman of the board of governors. Eva Lückes had been trained as a nurse first at the Middlesex Hospital and later at the Westminster where she had been taught according to Nightingale principles. When she applied for the job of matron at The London her knowledge of the hospital came from a brief period as night sister, and her chances of obtaining the post were not great. But she impressed the house committee, and succeeded in becoming the matron, at the very early age of 26, by virtue of her personality and the fact that she knew what she wanted to achieve. She took up her post in 1880. At the heart of her programme for the hospital were good management and high standards of care. Nurse training had been introduced already at The London; and under Miss Lückes' predecessor, Miss Swift, improvements had been made in practical nursing. What were needed however were more theoretical training, and better conditions for nurses. A course of lectures for nurses was introduced; Miss Lückes gave some and others were given by doctors on the staff. They were published under the title of *General Nursing*. Examinations were held, and the training period was reduced from three to two years. At the same time Miss Lückes began to tackle the low standard of accommodation and catering for her staff and by this means to attract women of better education and social status into the nursing profession. Another great change introduced by Eva Lückes in order to secure nurses from a different

social group was the introduction of payment for training. This was done at other hospitals – indeed she herself had been a 'paying probationer' at the Middlesex; and it was successful in raising the status of nursing. She also started a Preliminary Training School – the first in the country – which was situated in Tredegar House, Bow. The accommodation problem was solved unexpectedly by the construction of a railway line under the hospital estate which brought in £30,000 in 1884, much of which was used to build a home for nurses. Within a very short time Eva Lückes had not only stamped her personality on The London but had been responsible for major changes and improvements in the running of the hospital. She worked very hard herself and expected her staff to do the same.

Eva Lückes did, however, have critics and they were powerful ones. Her regime of training at The London, the long hours and the high standards of work she expected from her paying probationers, were the subject of much criticism in the press; and she was even required to defend herself in 1889 before a select committee of the House of Lords that was set up to examine the hospital system in London. Too much attention was focused on The London by this committee and the criticisms of it came mostly from individuals who had personal grievances. It was, however, attacked along with other voluntary hospitals (those supported by subscriptions and donations) for neglecting sections of the sick poor who were chronically ill or who could not obtain a governor's recommendation. Though eventually the select committee largely exonerated The London from any charges, it was difficult for the hospital to shake off press and public criticism of its approach to nurse training, and of its inability to cope with the pressures put on it by the local community.

The pressures could only be eased by greater investment in buildings and equipment. In 1890 a portico was added to the main entrance making a covered area which allowed shelter against the weather. But by the mid-1890s much more than this was needed; and, unfortunately, due to the bad publicity during the select committee sittings, not enough money was coming in. The London was over-stretching itself; it was trying to cope with too many patients on too few resources and with too little equipment. There was no electricity, and there were no laboratories and very poor facilities for isolation cases and for theatre work. As the nineteenth century drew to a close the hospital was urgently in need of two things – an injection of money, and governors who would restore confidence and optimism.

Sydney Holland possessed two outstanding gifts which he brought to The London in 1896. He was both a great leader and an outstanding fund-raiser. Indeed, he became known as 'The Prince of Beggars'. Holland was already known at The London and in

the East End for his work at Poplar Hospital for Accidents, where he was chairman. Poplar Hospital was one amongst many hospitals in the East End funded by a variety of means – by the poor rates, by charitable foundations, by subscription and by endowment. Some were workhouse infirmaries and were attached to parishes such as Mile End and Bethnal Green; some were for particular groups of sick persons, such as the East London Dispensary for Women and Children, or the East End Maternity Home, or, indeed, Poplar Hospital for Accidents. The London was different from all of these; it was the only teaching hospital, and it was by far the largest.

Sydney Holland came to The London largely as a result of persuasion by Eva Lückes. He had made a

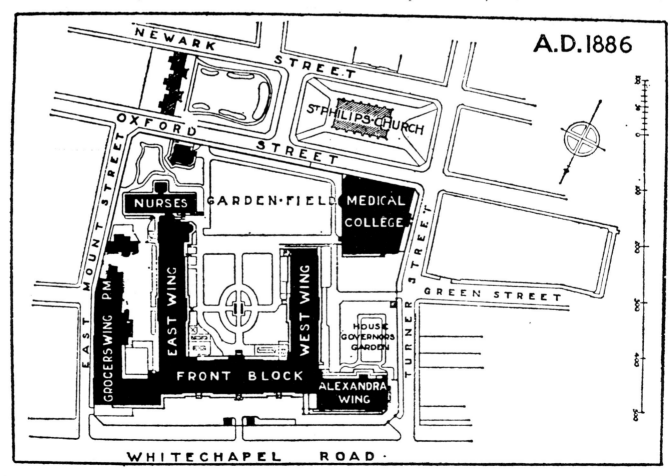

reputation for himself as an effective and active chairman of Poplar Hospital which was well respected and financially sound. He found the situation at The London much less satisfactory. Not only was the largest hospital under-equipped and lagging behind others in modern treatments, but it was also seriously under-funded. He found the place looking drab and there seemed to be a lack of enthusiasm in the work. Whilst there was important medical research going on in many departments – such as X-ray, pathology and physiology – the lack of space and facilities prevented the exploitation of it for patient care.

Holland presented the governors with a report on the appalling state of the hospital – the buildings, the equipment and morale – and suggested many improvements. Amongst these were additional space to be provided by adding extra storeys, specialist wards, more theatres, and better equipment. He also undertook to raise the money for these improvements. The house committee could not but follow his lead. The price they had to pay, however, was the introduction of charges for patients who could afford to pay something, and a major reorganization of the administration of the hospital. In this he had the support of Eva Lückes.

Without money, however, he could do nothing. He therefore set about raising large sums by seeking out large donations from rich contacts such as the ship-building magnate Alfred Yarrow and the Jewish bankers Rothschilds, and by a great letter-writing campaign. As soon as money came in it was spent and he returned immediately, like a beggar, to look for more. It was a dangerous but highly successful game and one which served The London well for many years, but left it dangerously short of reserves. It also earned him praise and envy in other hospitals, and made enemies for him in the growing number of organizations that were concerned with health care. Chief amongst these was Henry Burdett of the influential King Edward VII's Hospital Fund for London (King's Fund). In the last years of the nineteenth century and early years of the twentieth, Sydney Holland was to raise hundreds of thousands

of pounds by his 'begging', from John Fielden, James Hora, Benjamin Levy, Edward Raphael and many others whose names still survive in buildings and wards at The London. Their donations, however, were never sufficient and there was always a need to raise more money using novel and ingenious methods.

Sydney Holland's skill at raising money was matched by his aptitude for administration and organization. The reform of hospital administration had been a live issue for some years and had been spear-headed by professional medical groups. But towards the end of the century it was taken up by the Charity Organization Society and the King's Fund. The first conference of hospital administrators, governors, nurses and doctors was held in July 1893 at the Society of Arts in London. The London was far behind in this field and Sydney Holland recognized that sweeping changes had to be made. He appointed executive officers who were each responsible for co-ordinating the work of the sub-committees. It was not long, however, before E.W. Morris, whom Holland had first appointed as chief dispenser, showed himself to be a first-class administrator and at the earliest opportunity he was appointed house governor; this freed Holland for the more important duties of fund-raising and political bargaining.

Holland who had now succeeded to the title of 2nd Viscount Knutsford had established a close relationship with the Prince and Princess of Wales. They had already visited The London to open the library of the medical college and the new nurses' home, and the Princess of Wales had shown herself to be particularly interested in the work of the hospital; but the association deepened after Knutsford became chairman. This was due mainly to two events – the role of London Hospital nurses in the Boer War and the part played by London Hospital staff in operating on the Prince of Wales for appendicitis and nursing him back to health. The close connection with the Royal Family and the Princess of Wales, now Queen Alexandra, in particular, was to be vitally important – for morale, for fund-raising, and in attracting men and women of calibre. Indeed, Alexandra was soon to make her mark by her help in the introduction in 1899 of a new treatment from her own country, Denmark, the Finsen lamp for tuberculosis of the skin.

Lord Knutsford was bold in his schemes and the building programme which he advocated upon becoming chairman went ahead with speed. Between 1896 and 1906 a new isolation block had been built; new theatres, a new out-patients hall, a new nurses' home and two storeys on the main block had all been completed. But all this had cost £450,000 and Knutsford was never sure where the next thousand would come from. Despite having great success with appeals, the hospital still found it necessary to sell stock and land to keep the organization running. He was autocratic but because he was almost always right and achieved what he set out to do, and also because he possessed enormous charm, he was both liked and admired.

Lord Knutsford and Miss Lückes together made a formidable partnership. They were both strong characters who did not like opposition, and they were both devoted to their work and determined to see a job well done. Both were closely involved in the rebuilding of the hospital and in the establishment of nursing as a profession; but they were opposed to the introduction of registration of nurses which was being advocated in the early years of the twentieth century. Instead they proposed that each hospital should continue to issue its own certificate and that a national register of nurses should be kept, giving each one's qualification. It was not until the 1920s, and not without great opposition, that state registration was accepted at The London.

Medical practice and research were also flourishing at The London during the early years of the twentieth century. Miss Lückes' reform of nursing was matched by H.P. Dean's reform of teaching in the medical school. It was he who introduced specialists into the teaching of anatomy, physiology, pathology and bacteriology. The London attracted leading men in these fields who were able to teach and to build up great departments. Men such as Leonard Hill, physiologist, and William Bulloch,

bacteriologist, became famous and in turn attracted first-class students and money to the hospital. They were joined by Arthur Keith, Henry Head and James Mackenzie (anatomist, neurologist and cardiologist respectively) – who were also to contribute greatly to the reputation of the institution. Within ten years of his appointment Lord Knutsford had not only new buildings but also a first-class nursing and medical staff. In addition, in 1911, the Dental School opened to provide specialized treatment to local people as well as those referred from afar, and at the same time to give opportunities for training and research.

The training offered to students at The London did not differ greatly from that at other major London hospitals. All were required to undertake a five-year course prescribed by the General Medical Council in 1885 which would give them the knowledge sufficient to be safe general practitioners. They acquired this knowledge and experience from lectures and classes but mainly from watching surgeons and physicians in the wards and from dealing themselves with large numbers of patients with bad wounds or serious diseases. At The London the students were fortunate in their seniors and in the increasing support they received from larger numbers of better-trained nurses.

Neither medical students nor nurses, however, could escape infection in the wards or in their work in the local community. Both nurses and doctors were responsible for maternity care for a one-mile radius around the hospital. They were required to go out in all weathers to all kinds of homes, many of which were filthy and the source of infections of all kinds. The students worked very long hours and were often ill due to their work in the district and to fatigue arising from long stretches on duty. There was, however, a strong bond of loyalty to those with whom they worked and in particular to their 'firm', as the group around a consultant came to be called. This usually consisted of two physicians or surgeons, a house officer, and dressers, or clerks, who worked together normally over a period of three months. Staff and students both worked and played together – events such as annual picnics, races, and rowing were enjoyed as much by senior staff as by students. The relationship between staff and medical students was as crucial to the welfare of the student as it was to the success of the college and the smooth running of the hospital.

The hospital served a population that now stood at almost 600,000 – five times the level at the beginning of the nineteenth century; more than ever it was composed of immigrants, a large proportion of whom were Jewish and Irish. They had come to escape poverty, deprivation and persecution but found little on offer upon arrival in the East End. The hospital saw a great influx of patients suffering from industrial accidents and diseases such as tuberculosis, rheumatic fever, scarlet fever, that were the consequences of poor living and working conditions. The hospital now had 900 beds and was treating on average 15,000 in-patients and over 200,000 out-patients every year. Many amongst these were Jewish and they had their own wards and their own kitchens; and special provision was made for religious observances.

The London was at the height of its power and reputation when war broke out in 1914 with far-reaching consequences. Members of staff enlisted, students went off to fight, nurses went out to the front; and the hospital also had to cope with wounded from the continent and at home. The London became notable for taking in Belgian wounded after Lord Knutsford had been in Belgium

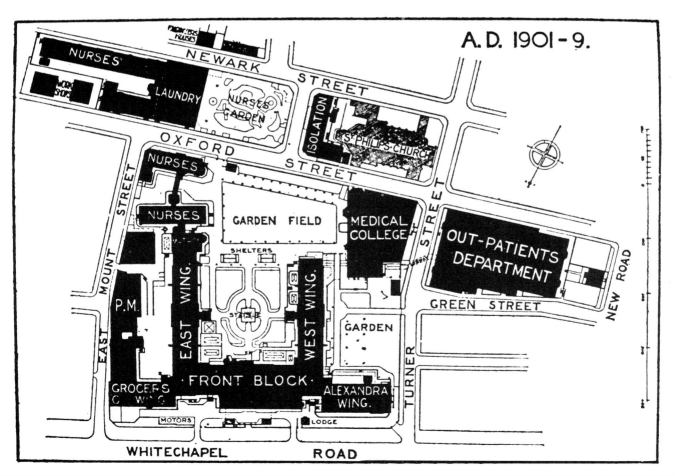

and seen the devastating effects of attack in the first few months. Knutsford, in fact, was to become deeply interested in and concerned about the effects of war upon the men, and he made a special plea in the House of Lords for the treatment of shell-shocked soldiers.

The war had many effects on the life of the hospital – women were admitted to the medical college to replace the students who had enlisted. The hospital faced another financial crisis as the war pushed up prices and took away money for donations – most people choosing to give to war charities. The war also brought fame, and death, to one of the most renowned 'Londoners' – Edith Cavell. She trained at The London and subsequently was matron of the first nurse training school in Belgium. The school was situated in Brussels which was at the centre of hostilities at the outbreak of the First World War, and Miss Cavell was involved in helping British soldiers brought in for treatment to escape back to

the allied lines. As a result she was arrested by the Germans on 5 August 1915, court-martialled and executed on 12 October 1915.

The hospital was also directly affected by attack when in 1916 bombs were dropped close by, killing and injuring many. The most testing event, however, was the bomb that fell on a munitions works in the East End in 1917; hundreds of dying and wounded were admitted to The London. It was a terrible event, but one which showed the hospital at its best. The war was followed by an influenza epidemic that gripped the country. Resources were low, people were weary after four years of war and the epidemic spread quickly; both nurses and patients fell victim to the epidemic and it left the hospital on its knees. As the war ended The London, in common with the other major hospitals, had to face not only a severely depleted staff but also a financial crisis that no amount of donations could solve.

III · Change and Challenge: 1919–1947

Though it is often simplistic and misleading to attribute to war great changes, the years 1918–1920 did indeed prove to be cataclysmic. The loss of so many men in the war, followed by the deaths due to influenza and the sorry state of the economy all combined to bring about changes in society. Some of these changes were felt keenly at The London and affected the financing of health care. Before the war the Insurance Act of 1912, providing for a rudimentary form of health insurance, had offered poor people some security of income when they needed hospital treatment, and there were plans to extend this scheme. Some thought was also given to the possible abolition of voluntary hospitals and their replacement by government-assisted institutions.

In the event neither the scheme for national health insurance nor that for replacing voluntary hospitals came to anything. The financing of health care, already under discussion before the war, now became an urgent matter. All hospitals had accumu-

lated huge debts and many were still caring for wounded. A government committee under Lord Cave was set up to look at the problem and the King's Fund made available large sums of money for the preservation of the voluntary hospital system. Of all the hospitals, The London was worst hit – its debt at the end of the war stood at £65,000 and subscriptions were not keeping pace with inflation. This situation resulted in the closure of wards, and a public outcry.

Lord Knutsford, however, was able to exploit the situation and turn it to the advantage of the hospital. Through a special appeal he secured £10,000 in donations and another large sum from the Cave Commissioners. At the same time an appeal was launched to aid all the voluntary hospitals and throughout 1922 money was raised for this purpose. The London benefited from the appeal but not as much as it had hoped and at the end of the year it still had a large debt. The quinquennial appeal in 1923, however, was a great triumph for Knutsford's fund-raising and by the end of that year £180,000 had been brought in through donations.

The London meanwhile was going through a process of change. The financial situation had an effect on the administration, and the death of Eva Lückes saw the end of an era. She was replaced by Miss Monk, highly competent but lacking the personality of her predecessor and less willing to move with the times; and times were changing. During the war years attitudes to women changed and advances in medicine occurred; but these shifts were not reflected in nursing organization and practice. There was reorganization of medical teaching and practice and the introduction of new treatments at The London. Insulin was introduced for the treatment of diabetes and ultra-violet light for some cases of tuberculosis; more laboratories, a larger X-Ray department and a massage department were also established; new men were elected to the medical staff – Arthur Ellis, George Riddoch, and Archie Clark-Kennedy among them.

Expansion and optimism were hard hit, however, by the General Strike of 1926. Although it lasted only a week, it had a profound effect on the country and a devastating effect on The London's finances: the 1928 appeal raised £120,000. The hospital, therefore, entered the depression years of the early 1930s in a very precarious financial position. The difficulties facing the hospital were compounded by Lord Knutsford's death in 1931. For 35 years he had been the guiding spirit in the hospital and his interest and energy had been unrivalled. It was a hard act to follow, particularly in difficult times, as his successor, Sir William Goschen, was only too ready to acknowledge.

Goschen took over not long after the crash of the American stock market and its consequent effect on the world economy. The 'great slump' had begun and with it all the adverse effects of unemployment, inflation and shrinking resources. The strides in medicine and surgery made during the early years of the twentieth century were now bringing demands for new buildings to house the specialist facilities.

Neuro-surgery and thoracic surgery both needed space for complicated and expensive treatments. Men such as Henry Souttar and Hugh Cairns were vocal in their demands for better facilities for their specialties. It was also an era of important discoveries in the field of bacteriology and pathology and the work done at The London by Florey, Bedson and Turnbull, while it greatly enhanced the hospital's reputation, also strained finances to the limit. It is clear, however, that the 1930s were a time of progress and energy at The London.

The decade also saw changes in the organization of nursing. After the war recruitment to nursing was good – perhaps due to the large number of spinsters; and retention was helped by the fact that The London had a rule barring from reappointment any member of the nursing staff who left. This led to stability and security for many, particularly the ward sisters who ruled in their own domain. It also led to some resistance to progress. However, with the appointment in 1935 of Clare Alexander as nurse tutor – The London's first qualified tutor – things began to change. She recognized the need for the system of training and examinations to be overhauled and for the state examination to be accorded more importance, and her enthusiastic approach began to affect the whole of the nursing staff of The London.

Nursing was also affected by the introduction to The London, in 1937, of a private wing. Hitherto, since the abolition by Lord Knutsford in 1897 of the patients' ticket system, all patients had been means-tested by answering questions concerning their income. Most were treated free; some had to pay a little. With the introduction of the private wing in 1937 the hospital tried to raise money by offering better rooms and more privacy to those who were able to pay. Private nursing was not new to The London for since the late 1880s it had private nursing staff. The Private Nursing Institution, as it was known, provided trained London Hospital nurses for the more affluent who preferred to be nursed at home. The Institution's strength averaged 200 between 1890 and 1948 and its nurses were employed not only in Britain but all over the world. The reputation of these nurses remained high for their standard of care as well as for their general conduct and appearance. George V was nursed by them and the registers of the institution show that they visited houses all over the Home Counties. They formed a separate body from the hospital nurses so were not a drain on staff resources at The London. Instead they provided revenue to equip the hospital. Funds were still tight – some wards remained closed; and patients still had to provide some basic foodstuffs. Despite the establishment of new medical and surgical units there was little money for improvements or building.

The work of the hospital at the end of the 1930s was, like most enterprises throughout the country, overshadowed by the unstable international situation. Already in 1938 plans for rearmament and civil-defence training were under way. The London, meanwhile, was approaching its bicentenary, and, despite the uncertain political and diplomatic situation, was planning celebrations and a major appeal. It was at this time that Mabel Reynolds was appointed matron. She had previously been matron of The London Clinic. She was more open and liberal than her predecessor, Miss Littleboy, and much more concerned about modern training and state qualifications: she appointed a group of qualified nurse tutors and abolished the grade of 'probationer' in favour of that of 'student nurse'. Daily life for the nurses did not change, for the formality and hier-archical nature of the profession remained. There was also little change at this period in the life of the medical students. On average 70 students per year (very few of whom were women) were educated; in general those who applied were accepted; they studied for a period of five years, a course that was in two parts – basic medical sciences and a clinical course. During the latter they came into daily contact with nurses, but social contact was much more difficult; indeed, if it was observed within the hospital it brought about a severe reprimand. This led to much ingenuity on the part of some of the medical students who endeavoured to spend more time in the wards than they were required to do.

Students' life, however, was not without enter-tainment in the form of sports and societies. The college's magazine *The London Hospital Gazette*, which was started in the nineteenth century, bears testimony to the wide range of events and experiences from which The London's students benefited. It was at Christmas particularly that hospital and college came together as a single community; staff took particular care that patients who were poor and lonely were not sent home at this time. All the staff stayed in the hospital for this great event. Decorations were hand-made; carol singing was organized by the nurses; the students produced the 'Christmas Show' and on Christmas Day, dressed as Father Christmas and the fairies, junior doctors would take gifts to all the patients and violets to the nurses. Senior and junior staff alike laid aside for a few days the formalities of normal life.

This formality was to be broken by the outbreak of war in 1939 and as The London approached its bicentenary it also faced the greatest challenge of its 200-year history. It was known that the capital would be a prime target for German attack, therefore the summer and autumn of 1939 were spent planning evacuation and setting up contingency plans for the running of the hospital – both for the core of staff that would be left in Whitechapel and for those groups who were to be evacuated.

The planning of the organization covered possible evacuation, fire-fighting, air-raid casualties, and staff training to fill places left by those who were called up. The Ministry of Health had its own ideas for coping with the wartime situation. It set up the Emergency Medical Service based on a plan to transfer most of the staff and facilities of the central London hospitals to outlying areas. Ten sectors were created radiating from Charing Cross, and The London was allocated sectors I and II which covered east and north-east London, Essex, and parts of Hertfordshire and Middlesex. Throughout the war the number of beds on the Whitechapel site remained at about 200, while certain types of case – such as maternity – were sent to one of the outlying areas.

Meanwhile within the hospital in Whitechapel, a series of major adaptations took place to cope with possible attacks. The main building was strengthened and protected, wards were turned over to dormitories; an emergency electricity supply was installed; and makeshift operating theatres were opened on the ground floor.

The first year of the war was a strange time for the hospital; all the preparations were made and everyone waited for the conflict – but nothing happened. Indeed some staff and equipment came back from outlying areas and their brief experience there had shown them how far advanced The London was in terms of equipment and treatment. One section of the work that increased and expanded was that of the clinic for venereal disease. The out-patient department of the Whitechapel Clinic, that had opened in 1926, expanded its activity to cope with the large number of seamen coming into the area.

Normal life was soon to be shattered by the relentless bombing of the capital that started in the summer of 1940. The London was well-prepared financially for attack as a result of money provided from increased taxation for the Emergency Medical Service – in fact for the first time for many years it was in credit. It was not long, however, before any thought of being in credit with a bright future of new buildings was buried beneath the workload of casualties and frightened people, and eventually beneath the rubble as bombs fell relentlessly on London, hitting the hospital in October 1940. At the same time the hospital had to cope with casualties from the surrounding areas. After some months of respite while German attention was turned to northern cities, bombing started again in March. The London was damaged, and again in May. The hospital was hit eight times, causing severe damage to some parts of the building, but no person was hurt at this time.

In 1941 Miss Reynolds resigned and Miss Clare Alexander, who was then matron of Addenbrookes Hospital, returned to The London as matron. The life of The London carried on as normally as possible and there was much traffic both in people and in correspondence between Whitechapel and outlying areas. An annexe was opened at Brentwood and the preliminary training for nurses was moved from its temporary home near Chelmsford to 'Trueloves' at Ingatestone in Essex to replace the school at Tredegar House which was now in the thick of the bombing. The disruption of training for both nurses and medical students, together with the hardships of rationing and severe winters, made life difficult during the years 1940–1943; the bombing and the besieged way of life came to be accepted. The hospital was run with great efficiency by the house governor Captain Henry Brierley and Miss Alexander and upon the death of William Goschen in 1943 John Mann, who was treasurer at that time, took over as chairman of the governors. He agreed to act in this capacity for the duration of the war.

Whilst the war was in progress talks began in earnest – they had been opened before the war but abandoned at its outset – to examine the possibility of reforming health care. Though discussions were in their infancy it was well known that many were anxious to bring the voluntary hospitals into a state system. William Goschen was in favour of greater cooperation with municipal hospitals (the old workhouse infirmaries) but totally opposed to the ending of the voluntary system, and in this he was at one with the governors.

The London and other 'voluntaries' had benefited greatly from payments under the Emergency Medical Service and were not in a strong position to argue against government financing and government control. Throughout the discussions on the introduction of a national health service The London was fearful of what this might mean, but too preoccupied with war and its aftermath to be able to devote much attention to it. The destruction of the East Wing in 1944 by a flying bomb did not delay the start of a new accident and orthopaedic department, and when Queen Mary visited The London in 1945 she is said to have been impressed by the signs of expansion and reconstruction. The hospital was by no means free from financial worries but it had received from government money during the war; and it was fortunate to receive a legacy of £105,000 from John Fielden who in 1901 had given £32,000 for an isolation block.

In 1946 the National Health Act received royal assent and was set to come into force in 1948. The years immediately following the war were, therefore, strange ones for The London, and indeed for all the voluntary hospitals. Work had to continue as normally as possible while repairs and reconstruction were undertaken; at the same time preparations were necessary in advance of major changes in administration underwritten by a completely new set of principles. It was well known, too, that there had been disagreements both within the government and with the doctors. There were difficulties not only as to how a national health service should operate, but whether indeed such a service should be imple-

mented at all. Meanwhile, until July 1948 arrived, the hospital still had to strive to raise money. In 1947, Sir John Mann was confirmed as chairman of the board of governors. The summer fair which was attended by Queen Mary, a loyal friend and helper to The London, raised £3,000 and a legacy from Sir Hugh Rigby, former senior surgeon, left the hospital £93,000; but with maintenance of £650,000 per annum and the cost of each patient at 13s.5d. per week, it was clear that legacies and summer fairs were never going to be enough. Indeed, for all the fears of the governors, many in the hospital were looking forward to the introduction of government control in the hope that it would remove much of the financial burden and allow them greater freedom to care for the sick and to advance medical teaching and research.

IV · The London and the NHS: 1948–1990

On 5 July 1948 the National Health Service became a reality. At The London Queen Mary resigned as President but became Patron; Sir John Mann resigned as chairman of the house committee, but became chairman of the board of governors, accountable to the Minister of Health. July 1948 was not, then, the watershed that it might have seemed at first. Indeed the NHS Act of 1946 and its implementation two years later were the culmination of 30 years of examination, discussion and planning around the question of a health service equally available to all. In the forefront of this planning was Bertrand Dawson, Lord Dawson of Penn, a physician at The London Hospital and to the King.

Following his experience of organizing medical services during the First World War, Dawson was commissioned by the Ministry of Health (newly established in 1919) to report on the provision of a comprehensive health service. His recommendations were based on a scheme he had proposed a year earlier in the Cavendish Lecture to the Royal Society of Medicine; these included local hospitals and clinics to be related to larger hospitals; teaching

hospitals to stand apart and serve the whole country; health care to be available to all as a matter of right; administrative matters to be determined by a board consisting of lay and medical members.

Despite modifications developed by the Nuffield Provincial Hospitals Trust in 1938, and by a Ministry of Health Committee in 1941, Dawson's proposals played a large part in forming the basis of the future National Health Service.

The proposals that were actually implemented in the Act included the funding of voluntary hospitals by public money and bringing them under public control. Despite fears to the contrary, The London and other teaching hospitals lost little of their independence in 1948. Not only were the same people in control, but the old system of committees linking nursing, medical and administrative personnel continued much as before; and although there was a certain amount of standardization and centralization in purchasing, the introduction of the NHS did not have a great effect on the daily life of The London.

A much greater impact was made by the medical

changes and discoveries – major advances had occurred during the war in the treatment of fractures, burns and tissue damage; plastic surgery had made enormous strides. The discovery of penicillin and other antibiotics meant that there was less need for beds for patients with infectious diseases including tuberculosis; basic nursing skills were combined with more technical care by nurses and with different ward routines. Likewise immunization reduced the demands for beds for poliomyelitis and diphtheria. The introduction of steroids, dialysis and new treatments for heart conditions not only revolutionized medical and nursing practices but affected the way in which the hospital was run. The London, along with all the large London teaching hospitals, offered a greater variety of expensive and successful treatments. People stayed in hospital for a shorter time but needed more staff to care for them. In addition, the hospital attracted more patients from long distances when their local general hospital did not have the facilities to care for them. There was at the same time a fall in the number of patients who came from the locality as the move of the population from the East End accelerated.

Increasing medical specialization and advances in technology also affected the training and education of other health professionals. Ever since the days of Eva Luckes The London had been in the forefront of educational advances in nursing and, having once accepted the concept of state registration, London Hospital nurses played a leading part in the work of the General Nursing Council as well as in other national and international nursing organizations.

Nurse training also underwent changes. There was more awareness of the total needs of the individual patient – physical, psychological, spiritual and social – and for continuity of care between hospital and community, and this had to be reflected in teaching. At the same time the staff had their own changing expectations in terms of their personal career and social life. The hospital staff as a whole was changing. Numbers had grown to compensate for the reduction of working hours and to allow for increased specialization and continuing training;

there were more married and part-time staff and a wider range of age and ability.

All this was not peculiar to The London, of course, but the hospital maintained its tradition of leading the way in meeting these changes and produced many notable 'firsts'. For example, during the 1950s and '60s several new nursing courses were started, including state enrolled training, an integrated general and psychiatric registration course and other specialized clinical courses. There was also introduced at this time a pioneering $4\frac{1}{2}$-year degree programme, to be followed later by other such academic programmes. There were developments also in midwifery and in other paramedical professions, all aimed at meeting new medical developments and changing needs of patients and staff.

The 1950s were a time of consolidation and reconstruction for all London hospitals. At The London the war-damaged buildings were repaired and rebuilt, and new buildings were added. In 1953 the dental department was completed, and in 1957 Knutsford House, a block of flats for nursing sisters, was finished, offering the best accommodation for nurses in London. Indeed, one of the ways in which The London tried to attract and retain staff was by upgrading and building new residences. Money for this work came partly from the so-called 'free funds', or legacies and donations to the hospital that were not subject to Ministry of Health control, and partly from public funds.

By the end of the decade, in common with other large hospitals, The London began to see differences in personnel and in attitudes. As the 1960s began the hospitals had accommodated the changes ushered in by the NHS and found themselves with enough money and the enthusiasm of younger staff to be able to exploit fully the increasing number of advances in medicine. One of these major advances, cardiac resuscitation, completely changed accepted staffing arrangements. The need to have at all times a certain number of trained staff available as a group to deal with cardiac arrest affected the organization of nursing and medical rotas and the running of wards and departments. The introduction of computers also revolutionized certain work practices. The London was in the forefront of this modernization and took part in several experimental projects.

It also took part in a study which examined the administration of drugs to hospital patients and was responsible for pioneering a major change in methods. The 1960s was a decade in which much was happening scientifically and technologically and in which society was changing; opportunities could be quickly exploited as money was readily available.

It was at this time also that Mile End and St Clement's Hospitals and later Bethnal Green Hospital joined The London. At the same time Brentwood Annexe, held in great affection by so many Lon-

doners, was closed. The Minister of Health announced plans for changes in London health care at the same time as the University of London called for changes in medical education. The hospital and the medical college were to be affected and the next five years saw successive attempts to reform administrative structures. In addition, the advent of the microchip brought other challenges.

In 1972 a White Paper on health service reorganization was issued, its main aim being to integrate the various branches of health care. For The London however, as for the other teaching hospitals, it meant the end of their virtual independence. When the Act was finally passed in 1974 the Board of Governors

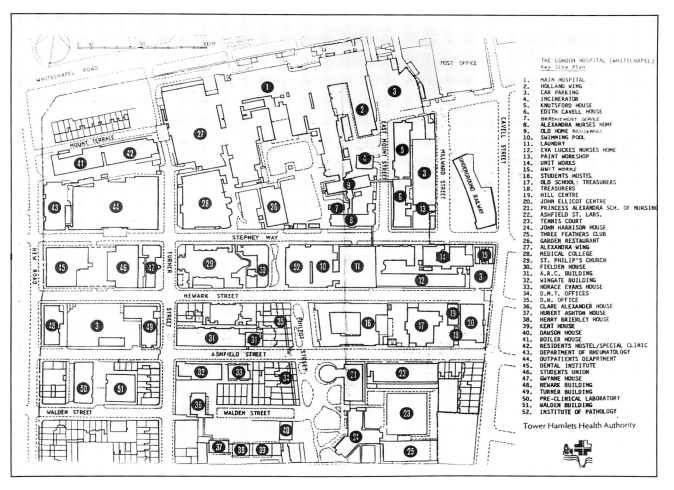

was replaced by a management team which in turn was answerable to an Area Health Authority (City & East London), thence to a Regional Health Authority (North East Thames) and from there to the Department of Health and Social Security. It was at this time also that the special trustees of The London Hospital were established (as in other hospitals) by the Secretary of State. Their remit was, and still is, to administer the endowment funds and properties of The London Hospital, including the three sites of Whitechapel, Mile End and St Clement's. Old jobs went, new jobs were created and many familiar faces disappeared. It was at this point that central government authority really began to be felt at The London and that the ethos of the old voluntary hospital changed. The hospital was also affected greatly by external factors; the oil crisis of the early 1970s and its effect on the world economy imposed financial stringency on the whole of the public sector. This in turn led to industrial unrest which culminated in the first major strike by health workers – an event which had a profound effect on attitudes within the institution.

The work of all the major teaching hospitals continued to develop and expand in the 1970s, but the pace slowed considerably as inflation imposed cuts in funding and staffing levels. In addition, all the capital's teaching hospitals saw money being channelled out of London to major provincial hospitals in an attempt to equalize standards particularly in hospital facilities and consultant posts; and it also saw much tighter budgetary controls with the introduction of an annual financial cycle. Communications with the department were often slow and decision-making protracted with the result that the hospital sometimes seemed to be losing direction. At the same time, the area it served was changing rapidly and the new wave of immigrants, mostly from Asia, brought with them new health and social problems.

Problems within the administration were also reflected in the college. The college had to look towards its relationship with the University of London (of which it had been a constituent part since the beginning of the century) as well as to that with the area health authority. Growing numbers of students and problems of finance forced the college to examine its own administration. The working party that was set up to do this had to work quickly and the changes it recommended in organization and courses were pushed through in haste. Closer cooperation between the medical colleges at The London, St Bartholomew's, and Queen Mary College, recommended by the Todd Report on Medical Education in 1969, and welcomed by The London (the BLQ option), was put to one side.

Criticism of the new system and the unease and unhappiness it provoked led to a re-examination of health care throughout London and across the country during the years 1979 to 1982. In 1982 the area health authorities which seemed cumbersome were disbanded and much of the management and planning devolved to health districts which corresponded with those of local authorities. Thus The London moved closer to its local community and at the same time continued to develop specialist services such as cardiac medicine, gastroenterology, nephrology and neurosurgery. It also continued to develop its nurse education and to build up the Princess Alexandra College of Nursing. In addition, plans for joint development between the medical colleges at The London and Bart's, linked with Queen Mary College, became a reality, beginning with new joint departments and projects. A major event for the hospital was the opening by the Queen of the new Alexandra Wing in March 1982, after eight years of difficulties and financial struggle. The wing contained new theatres, an X-ray department, a sterile services department and an emergency department which provided casualty services for the locality. In 1984 another change occurred with the nationwide abolition of multi-disciplinary consensus management teams and the introduction of the concept of general management.

In the 1990s the hospital looks forward to further changes and opportunities. They include the introduction of a helicopter emergency service, the building of a new unit for children, the amalgamation of the College of Nursing with the School of Nursing in Newham in a move towards training for health care in the year 2000 and beyond, the establishment of a new joint centre for medical education for St Bartholomew's Hospital, Queen Mary College and The London adjoining The London Hospital, Mile End. In addition, the hospital is having to consider the possibility of fundamental alterations in its governance.

The aim of achieving and maintaining the highest standards in diagnosis, advice and treatment continues to be the main priority at The London. At the same time, teaching and research are fostered and encouraged wherever possible. The London provides an intellectual and physical environment in which successful research can flourish to the benefit of patients. The many innovations include, for instance, the development of a vaccine to lessen the incidence of periodontal disease, fundamental research into the nature of inflammation, particularly in disorders of joints and in the gastrointestinal tract, successful innovations in cardiac, brain and joint replacement surgery, ingenious applications in therapeutic endoscopy, and increasingly effective treatments for infectious diseases, blood disorders and many forms of cancer. Such a list is inevitably selective but serves to indicate that much important work is being done at The London.

The London Hospital was founded in 1740 to serve the needs of 'the manufacturing and seafaring classes' – the East Enders of the time. For 250 years it has kept faith with this resolve and purpose. Whatever developments are in prospect, The London will continue to serve its community and the nation.

The London Hospital
Illustrated

I · From Infirmary to Hospital: 1740–1854

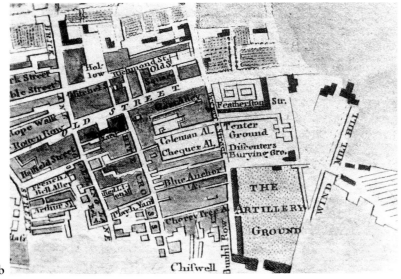

c

d

I 1. Founding of the London Infirmary, Featherstone Street

A meeting attended by seven men at the Feathers Tavern, Cheapside, on 23 September 1740 (the minutes of which are shown here (*a*)) led to the founding of the London Infirmary, and the first hospital was accommodated for a few months in a leasehold house in Featherstone Street (*b*), near Old Street. John Harrison, aged only 22 when the hospital was founded, and the institution's first surgeon (*c*), took the main initiative and provided the thrust and energy for the enterprise. He died at 35. John Andrée, of Huguenot descent, was the Infirmary's first physician (*d*); he remained in office 24 years.

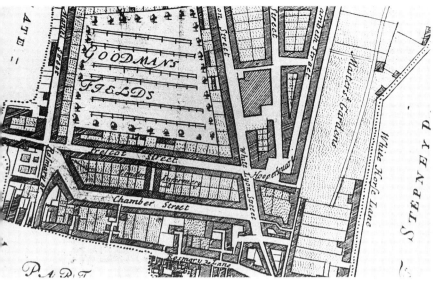

b

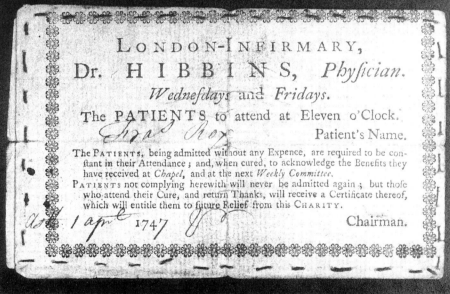

d

I 2. The London Infirmary, Prescot Street

In May 1741 the London Infirmary moved to new premises in Prescot Street near the Mint and to the north-east of the Tower (a). Records suggest that the buildings were flanked by public houses. The surrounding area had a reputation for poverty and for low entertainment, represented here by Hogarth's Gin Lane (b) and by a scene from a contemporary print (c)*. At the time, and over the next century, the recommendation of a hospital governor was necessary before a patient was allowed to attend the hospital. On this ticket (d) issued to patients the requirements to offer thanks after cure were stated.

*Made available and photographed by courtesy of Tower Hamlets Borough Archives.

I 3. The house committee's concerns

This painting, by a current member of staff* of the hospital, is based on written descriptions of the four houses in Prescot Street which made up the London Infirmary. It provided 130 beds.

The hospital's archives indicate clearly that the main problem for the house committee at this time was the hiring of suitable women as nurses. Those employed were, for the most part, elderly and it is recorded that some were of uncertain sobriety or had doubtful pasts. Indeed the first matron, Ann Looker, was dismissed for misconduct. She was succeeded by Mrs Broad who remained in office for 15 years and died shortly before the infirmary moved to Whitechapel.

The conditions in which Mrs Broad and her nurses had to work were far from ideal. Patients were often infested with lice and behaved in an unruly manner; the houses themselves were ridden with woodworm. The lack of running water and sanitation added to the unsavoury nature of the place which began to draw complaints from the local inhabitants.

The house committee then moved to improve matters: money was spent on repairing and converting the houses and rules were made for the nurses who were required to 'attend the patients diligently' and 'behave with tenderness to the patients and with courtesy and respect to strangers'.

*Professor J.P. Blandy, FRCS

I 4. Four early presidents of the London Infirmary

John Harrison persuaded the second Duke of Richmond (*a*) to take an interest in the London Infirmary from its beginning. He was described as 'the most humane and best living man, . . . noble in his way of acting, talking and thinking'. As the London Infirmary's first president, he gained for it the interest of great officers of state and of members of the House of Lords; he also started the close association between the hospital and the Royal Family. Edward, Duke of York, became the hospital's first royal president in 1765 (*b*) and below him is Henry, Duke of Gloucester (president 1767–1805)(*c*). William Cavendish, Duke of Devonshire (*d*) succeeded his father in the office in 1755, and presided over the beginning of the new hospital in Whitechapel.

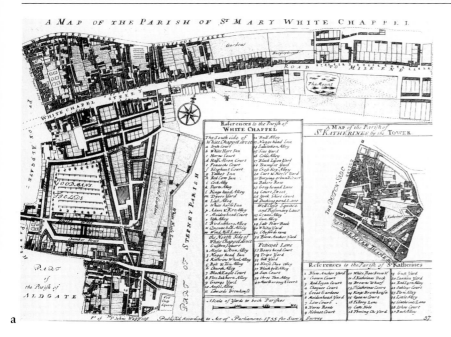

I 5. The parish of St Mary, Whitechapel

This map of the parish of St Mary, Whitechapel (*a*) was published in 1755. The site of the new London Hospital just east of the Mount is shown as an empty space. Although building had started in 1752, progress was intermittent because of limited funds, and the new hospital did not open until 1757. By this time the necessity to move from Prescot Street, shown just south of Goodman's Fields, had become urgent.

The eighteenth-century church of St Mary Matfelon was the second to have been built on the site: the origin of 'Matfelon' is obscure (*b*). The Mount was a saxon earthwork, built to defend London, and became a place for outings and sightseeing. The picture shows The London Hospital next to the Mount (*c*), before the latter's removal in 1830, when all the earth was taken away in hand-carts.

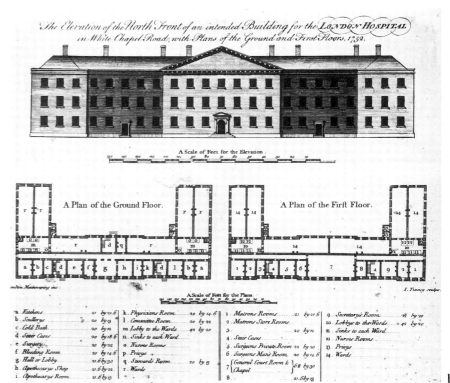

The Elevation of the North Front of an intended Building for the LONDON HOSPITAL in White Chapel Road; with Plans of the Ground and First Floors. 1752.

A Scale of Feet for the Elevation.

A Plan of the Ground Floor.

A Plan of the First Floor.

A Scale of Feet for the Plans.

a. Kitchens	21 by 21.6	k. Physicians Room	20 by 14.6	1. Matrons Rooms	21 by 21.6	9. Secretarys Room	22 by 20
b. Sculleryes	20 by 13	l. Committee Room	20 by 22	2. Matrons Store Rooms		10. Lobbys to the Wards	42 by 20
c. Cold Bath	20 by 11	m. Lobby to the Wards	42 by 20	3.	20 by 11	11. Sinks to each Ward	
d. Stair Cases	20 by 18.6	n. Sinks to each Ward		4. Stair Cases		12. Nurses Rooms	
e. Surgery	20 by 22	o. Nurses Rooms		5. Surgeons Private Room	22 by 20	13. Privys	
f. Bleeding Room	20 by 14.6	p. Privys		6. Surgeons Mans Room	20 by 14.6	14. Wards	
g. Hall or Lobby	21.6 by 30	q. Stewards Room	20 by 13	7. {General Court Room & Chapel}	68 by 30		
h. Apothecarys Shop	21.6 by 22	r. Wards		8.	21.6 by 30		
i. Apothecarys Room	21.6 by 13						

b

Boulton Mainwaring inv:

J. Tinney sculps.

I 6. Planning the new London Hospital, Whitechapel

In 1745 George Parker, second Earl of Macclesfield and president of the Royal Society (*a*), became chairman of a committee set up by the governors to procure suitable land 'in the cheapest and best manner they can' for the building of the new hospital. The elevation and plans of the new building (*b*), drawn up by Boulton Mainwaring, are shown with a picture of the imaginary new London Hospital (*c*), engraved and printed (by William Bellers) to encourage subscribers to the charity (*d*).

I 7. The Hospital Charter

In 1757 a petition was made for the hospital to become incorporated. This allowed the governing body to purchase lands and take out leases without having to appoint individuals as trustees. It was the first stage in a long process of expansion of the hospital site.

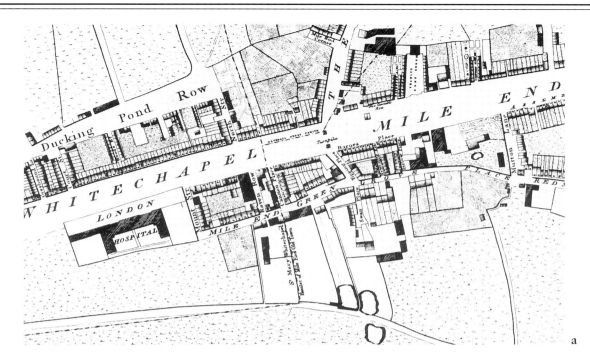

a

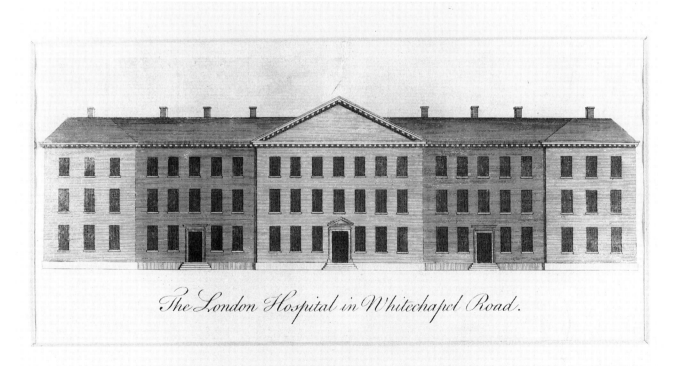

The London Hospital in Whitechapel Road.

b

I 8. Expansion of the hospital

The new London Hospital in Whitechapel, as planned by Boulton Mainwaring 26 years previously, was completed with the building of the east wing (1775) and finally the west wing (1778). The map (*a*) and the drawing (*b*) show The London Hospital as William Blizard would have known it when he was elected to the staff in 1780.

a

b

I 9. Contemporary Whitechapel

As a contrast to the Georgian design of The London, an older building (1695), also of architectural distinction, still stands in Mile End Road and is little altered from the original (*a*). Trinity Almshouses were built for 'decayed masters and commanders of ships and ye widows of such'. This was one of many charities apart from The London in which Blizard took an interest. The print by Rowlandson (*b*) depicts the scene at Mile End turnpike at the beginning of the nineteenth century.

b

I 10. Sir William Blizard's inspiration and influence

William Blizard, portrayed here by Opie at the height of his long career (*a*), was described as tall and thin, with strongly marked features and a vigorous and active mind. As a surgeon he cautioned against too much enthusiasm for amputations, and forbade the use of cautery, which was still traditionally applied to wounds by means of branding irons. Nelson and his navy benefited from his advice. Like his friend, the prison and hospital reformer John Howard, Blizard was a man of ideas and ideals, a philanthropist and reformer.

The memorial to John Howard, who wrote a detailed report on The London, is in St Paul's Cathedral (*b*).

a

b

c

d

I 11. John Ellicott, FRS

The London Hospital was fortunate to have John Ellicott (1706–1772) as an early friend, benefactor and governor (a). He was the most distinguished member of a celebrated family of clock- and watchmakers (b) in the City, and his home was at St John's, Hackney. As well as being a craftsman he was a notable scientist, mathematician, astronomer and close friend of Benjamin Franklin, the American statesman (c). He designed and constructed a seal for the hospital which incorporated the idea of the Good Samaritan as well as the hospital's link with the City of London (d). In modified form this has remained as an emblem of the hospital and of the medical college, and serves as a memorial to Ellicott.

In as much as ye have done it unto one of the least of these my Brethren ye have done it unto me. Mat: 25 v: 40.

a W: Hogarth Inv. et Delin.

b

I 12. William Hogarth's support for The London Hospital

The great eighteenth century artist William Hogarth was a man of generosity who, throughout his career, showed sympathy for poor and suffering humanity: he was a friend and benefactor of several London hospitals. The London Hospital possesses Hogarth's drawing of Christ gesturing towards an imaginary hospital which provided the background for his statement on the Last Judgement (a). The drawing formed the basis of a series of engravings (b) which were used to gain publicity for the good work of the hospital.

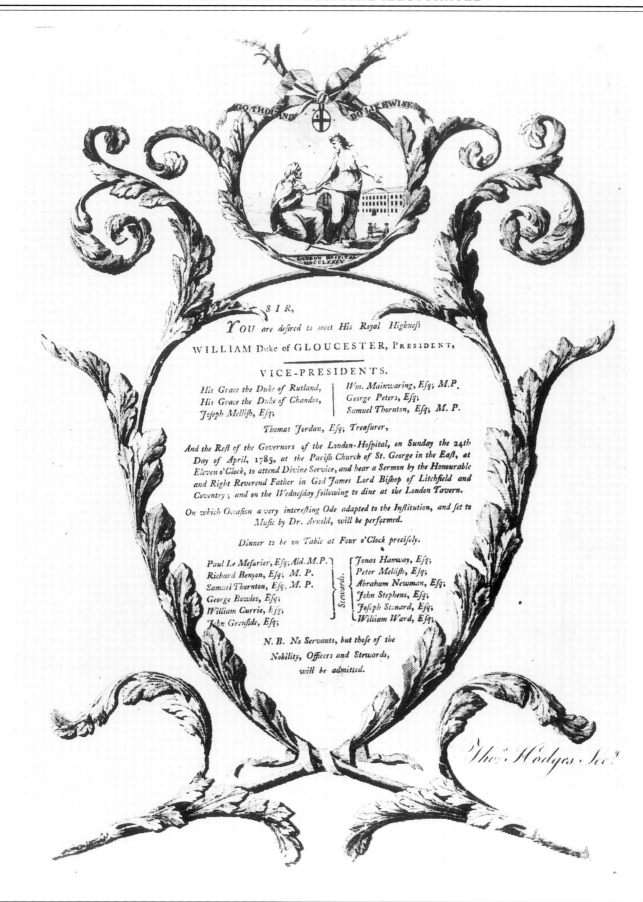

GO THOU AND DO LIKEWISE

LONDON HOSPITAL
MDCCLXXV

SIR,

YOU are desired to meet His Royal Highness

WILLIAM Duke of GLOUCESTER, President,

VICE-PRESIDENTS.

His Grace the Duke of Rutland,	*Wm. Mainwaring, Esq; M.P.*
His Grace the Duke of Chandos,	*George Peters, Esq;*
Joseph Mellish, Esq;	*Samuel Thornton, Esq; M.P.*

Thomas Jordan, Esq; Treasurer,

And the Rest of the Governors of the London-Hospital, on **Sunday the 24th**
Day of April, 1785, *at the Parish Church of St. George in the East, at*
Eleven o'Clock, to attend Divine Service, and hear a Sermon by the Honourable
and Right Reverend Father in God James Lord Bishop of Litchfield and
Coventry; and on the Wednesday following to dine at the London Tavern.

On which Occasion a very interesting Ode adapted to the Institution, and set to
Music by Dr. Arnold, will be performed.

Dinner to be on Table at Four o'Clock precisely.

Paul Le Mesurier, Esq; Ald. M.P.	*Jonas Hanway, Esq;*
Richard Benyon, Esq; M. P.	*Peter Mellish, Esq;*
Samuel Thornton, Esq; M. P.	*Abraham Newman, Esq;*
George Bowles, Esq;	*John Stephens, Esq;*
William Currie, Esq;	*Joseph Stonard, Esq;*
John Grenside, Esq;	*William Ward, Esq;*

Stewards.

N. B. No Servants, but those of the
Nobility, Officers and Stewards,
will be admitted.

Thos. Hodges, Sec.

a

b

I 13. The Annual Feast (opposite)

John Harrison instituted the annual feast as a means of raising money and of gaining publicity for the hospital. Invitations were issued to the governors and subscribers to attend a church service and procession followed by a feast. The invitations were ornate and differed in design each year. This example shows a variation on the theme of the Good Samaritan, which was a powerful emblem at the start of the voluntary hospital movement, which continues to this day at The London Hospital.

I 14. The founders of the Medical College

The joint founders of the London Hospital Medical College which opened in October 1785 were John Maddocks, physician (a), and William Blizard, surgeon (b). As England's first complete medical school, it was a venture of originality and enterprise, depending particularly on Blizard's reforming zeal, vision and determination. It was founded with the primary purpose of improving medical education, but additional benefits to the hospital and medical services in the East End during the past two centuries have been inestimable.

a

Take care of him and whatsoever thou spendest more, when I come again I will repay thee.

b

I 15. Founding of the Samaritan Society

William Blizard (*a*) was described as having 'a character that happily unites science with benevolence, and professional skill with the exercise of humanity'. His concern about the lack of any provision for patients when they left hospital and the considerable distress that often resulted, led him to contribute extensively from his own pocket. In 1791 he conceived the idea of establishing a Samaritan Society with the motto 'take care of him' (*b*). The work rapidly expanded to meet such needs as supplying patients with spectacles, artificial limbs, items of clothing, and trusses. In 1795 it was recorded that 'many poor patients in The London Hospital, after they had been cured of their diseases and were in a state of convalescence, had been supplied with necessaries and enabled to return home and renew their occupations'. The Samaritan Society continues to apply the philanthropic ideals and endeavours of William Blizard and, along with the London Hospital Medical College, is a living memorial to him.

AN

ESSAY

ON THE

SHAKING PALSY.

BY

JAMES PARKINSON,
MEMBER OF THE ROYAL COLLEGE OF SURGEONS.

LONDON:
PRINTED BY WHITTINGHAM AND ROWLAND,
Goswell Street,

FOR SHERWOOD, NEELY, AND JONES,
PATERNOSTER ROW.
1817.

c

I 16. James Parkinson

The name of James Parkinson (1755–1824) is known throughout the world for his description of 'paralysis agitans', the shaking palsy (*a*), now known universally as 'Parkinson's disease'. He became a pupil at The London Hospital in 1776, and like his father, and subsequently his son, worked as an apothecary in nearby Hoxton. He had an active and original mind, and radical political views, and was a prolific writer, as well as providing excellent service to the local community. Also a very keen amateur geologist, he made important contributions in that subject as well as in medicine (*b*). No portrait of James Parkinson survives but an illustration from the frontispiece of one of his books shows an apothecary of the time warning of the consequences of drinking excessive alcohol (*c*).

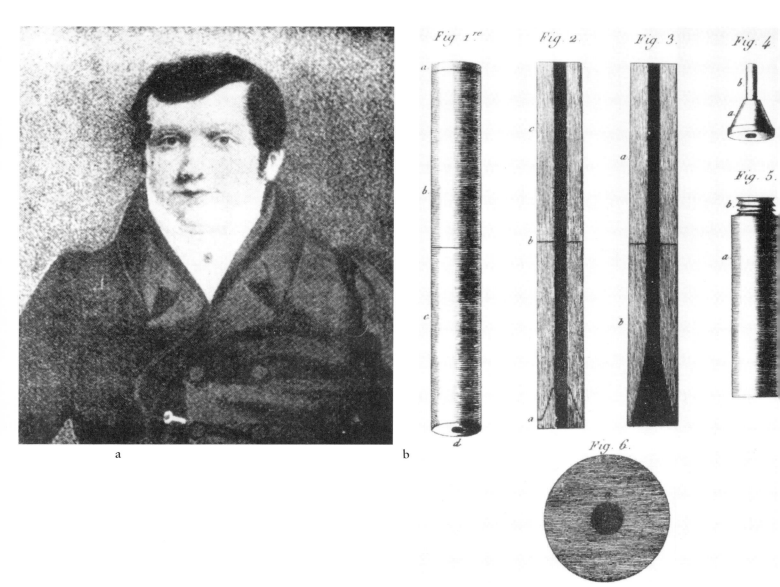

a   b

I 17. Thomas Davies, pioneer in the use of the stethoscope

Dr Thomas Davies (1792–1839), a Welshman (a), became a pupil at The London Hospital under the direction of his uncle, who was apothecary to the hospital. He practised for two years locally at Mile End, but his health deteriorated and he was advised to seek a southern climate as a means of helping his consumption. After a time at Montpelier in southern France, he improved sufficiently to become a student in

Paris at the Necker Hospital, where Laennec taught his new method of diagnosis by auscultation (listening to the heart and lungs, (b)). When he returned to London he was perhaps the first in Britain to lecture on Laennec's great innovation. He himself died of pulmonary tuberculosis at the age of 47 and was buried in the churchyard of St Botolph's in the City.

I 18. John Yelloly, FRS

John Yelloly (1774–1842), an Edinburgh graduate, settled in London in 1780. He was physician at The London from 1807 to 1818 and later physician to the Norfolk and Norwich Hospital. He is remembered particularly as one of the originators of the Royal Medical and Chirurlogical Society, destined many years later to become the Royal Society of Medicine. At The London he prepared the hospital's first pharmacopoeia, to be printed at the expense of the hospital, in order to economize in dispensing. A similar publication, *The London Hospital Formulary*, was reintroduced in 1982.

I 19. Archibald Billing, FRS

Archibald Billing (1791–1881), a native of Dublin, started teaching at The London in 1817, and was elected physician in 1822. His most notable contribution to The London was his inclusion of regular bedside teaching as part of clinical instruction, the first course of its kind in England. He was an accomplished, cultured and influential man, and founder member of the University of London senate. He is thought to have been the last physician in London to visit his patients on horseback.

I 20. Jonathan Pereira, FRS

Jonathan Pereira (1804–1853) was born in Shoreditch. He started his professional life as an apothecary, became lecturer in chemistry and later physician at The London. In 1842, he was made first professor of 'materia medica' to the Pharmaceutical Society, and was foremost in placing the knowledge and use of drugs on a scientific basis. He died as a result of an accident while at the height of his career. A memorial service for him was held in the hospital chapel, the first recorded tribute of its kind to a member of the medical staff.

I 21. Operation room (1837)

Illustrations of operating theatres as they existed before the use of anaesthesia and the application of antisepsis are rare. This watercolour of the theatre at The London in the early nineteenth century is particularly vivid. Little imagination is required to appreciate the horror and suffering endured by patients when undergoing procedures such as amputation and cutting to remove bladder stones, even though surgeons usually operated with lightning speed. Patients were led in blindfold and held on the wooden table by strong assistants, while the surgeon in his frock coat performed the operation. Additional sawdust was called for when excessive bleeding had filled the tray seen at the foot of the operating table.

b

I 22. Curling and Scott: two eponymous surgeons

Thomas Blizard Curling (1811–1888) (*a*) and John Scott (1799–1846) (*b*), both former pupils of William Blizard, became surgeons at The London in the first half of the nineteenth century. Each made important contributions and in the process became eponymous. Curling discovered a relationship between burns and duodenal ulceration, and his name is still used to describe this form of stress ulcer. Scott's name was recalled in a more ephemeral manner for a dressing which, for over a century, was a favourite application.

a

b

I 23. William John Little, pioneer of orthopaedic surgery

A book entitled *Mender of the Maimed* was written in 1919 by Sir Arthur Keith, a distinguished anatomist at The London. In it he relates the story of William John Little (1810–1894) who was born in the East End (*a*). As a child Little had what must have been poliomyelitis, leaving his left foot deformed. While a student at The London and after he became a surgeon (*b*), Little constantly searched for ways in which such deformities might be helped, particularly after his own club foot was alleviated by tenotomy, a procedure carried out by Stromayer, a German surgeon. Little published widely on the subject and went on to establish what was later to become the Royal National Orthopaedic Hospital. He is regarded as the pioneer of orthopaedic surgery in Britain.

I 24. London labour and the London poor

In the mid-nineteenth century Henry Mayhew, author and joint editor of *Punch*, published a series of articles with the title *London Labour and the London Poor*, the text of which was accompanied by numerous illustrations. These show people and scenes which would have been encountered in the vicinity of The London Hospital at that time.

a

b

I 25. Shipbuilding and the docks

By the late eighteenth century the docks in the Port of London were hopelessly congested, inadequate and incapable of meeting the demands of industrialization and the growing empire. A response to these problems came in the early years of the nineteenth century from private companies, which built several enclosed yards on land south of The London Hospital. They included the massive developments of St Katherine's, the London and West India Docks.

A picturesque scene of the new docks is shown (a): the illustration by Gustav Doré later in the century conveys a more realistic picture of dockworkers in the East End (b).

I 26. The Steam Age arrives in Whitechapel

Whitechapel High Street is seen here (a) in an engraving by J.H. Shepherd (1837). It is a somewhat romantic representation. As the main road out of the city to Essex it was always busy and Stow had commented that it was shabby and 'no small blemish to so famous a city'. In addition, there was a haymarket on the street, which continued until 1927, and the neighbourhood contained many slaughterhouses.

A cartoonist caricatured the arrival of steam in Whitechapel (b)*. He was however premature to portray major changes in road transport and the local way of life: it was the internal combustion engine that eventually replaced horse-drawn transport after the First World War.

*Reproduced by kind permission of the London Borough of Tower Hamlets

a

b

c

I 27. Bells of Whitechapel

The Whitechapel Bell Foundry (*a*) was established in Houndsditch in 1420 and moved to its present site in Whitechapel Road in 1738, nineteen years before the nearby London Hospital first received patients. Many of the world's most famous bells, including Big Ben, Bow Bells and America's original Liberty Bell were cast there. Bells were also made for The London. They include the large bell (*b*) now in the main entrance of the hospital, and a bell, known as the operation bell, which was made in 1791 (*c*). The latter was rung to summon attendants to restrain patients when undergoing operations half a century before anaesthetics were available.

II · The London Makes its Mark: 1855–1918

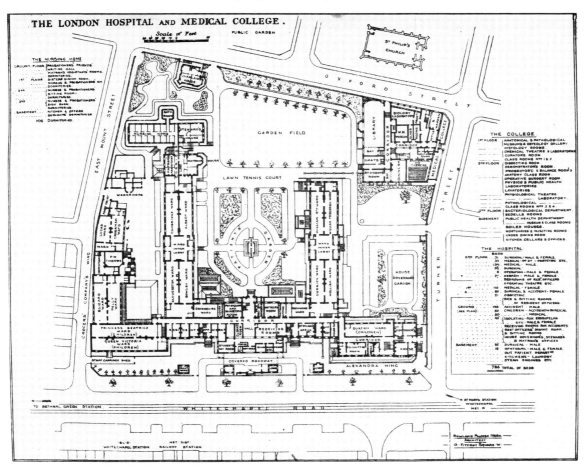

His Majesty's Privy Council having approved of precautions proposed by the Board of Health in London, on the alarming approach
OF THE

INDIAN CHOLERA

It is deemed proper to call the attention of the Inhabitants to some of the Symptoms and Remedies mentioned by them as printed, and now in circulation.

Symptoms of the Disorder;

Giddiness, sickness, nervous agitation, slow pulse, cramp beginning at the fingers and toes and rapidly approaching the trunk, change of colour to a leaden blue, purple, black or brown; the skin dreadfully cold, and often damp, the tongue moist and loaded but flabby and chilly, the voice much affected, and respiration quick and irregular.

REMEDIES;

All means tending to restore circulation and to maintain the warmth of the body should be had recourse to without the least delay.

The patient should be immediately put to bed, wrapped up in hot blankets, and warmth should be sustained by other external applications, such as repeated frictions with flannels and camphorated spirits, poultices of mustard and linseed (equal parts) to the stomach, particularly where pain and vomiting exist, and similar poultices to the feet and legs to restore their warmth. The returning heat of the body may be promoted by bags containing hot salt or bran applied to different parts, and for the same purpose of restoring and sustaining the circulation white wine wey with spice, hot brandy and water, or salvolatile in a dose of a tea spoon full in hot water, frequently repeated; or from 5 to 20 drops of some of the essential oils, as peppermint, cloves or cajeput, in a wine glass of water may be administered with the same view. Where the stomach will bear it, warm broth with spice may be employed. In every severe case or where medical aid is difficult to be obtained, from 20 to 40 drops of laudanum may be given in any of the warm drinks previously recommended.

These simple means are proposed as resources in the incipient stages of the Disease, until Medical aid can be had.

THOS. KEY,
GEO. TINDALL, } Churchwardens.

Sir GILBERT BLANE, Bart in a pamphlet written by him on the subject of this Disease, recommends persons to guard against its approach by moderate and temperate living, and to have in readiness, the prescribed remedies, and in case of attack to resort thereto immediately but the great preventative he states, is found to consist in a due regard to Cleanliness and Ventilation

a

BOARD OF WORKS
FOR THE LIMEHOUSE DISTRICT.
COMPRISING LIMEHOUSE, RATCLIFF, SHADWELL & WAPPING.

In consequence of the appearance of **CHOLERA** within this District, the Board have appointed the under-mentioned Medical Gentlemen who will give ADVICE, MEDICINE, AND ASSISTANCE, FREE OF ANY CHARGE, AND UPON APPLICATION, AT ANY HOUR OF THE DAY OR NIGHT.

The Inhabitants are earnestly requested not to neglect the first symptoms of the appearance of Disease, (which in its early stage is easy to cure), but to apply, WITHOUT DELAY, to one of the Medical Gentlemen appointed.

The Board have opened an Establishment for the reception of Patients, in a building at Green Bank, near Wapping Church, (formerly used as Wapping Workhouse), where all cases of Cholera and Diarrhœa will be received and placed under the care of a competent Resident Medical Practitioner, and proper Attendants.

II 1. Epidemics of cholera

In a succession of epidemics which spread across Europe from the east in the nineteenth century, cholera struck severely among the poor and destitute who lived in overcrowded and insanitary conditions in the East End. Public notices were used to give warning and advice to local inhabitants (a). The epidemics eventually became a powerful influence for reform (b), leaving no alternative but to acknowledge the inadequacy of housing, water supplies, sanitation, hospitals and cemeteries.

a

b

II 2. The administration of the hospital

The hospital has been fortunate in having some very able and dedicated men as governors and house governors during its history. William Nixon (a) was appointed house governor in 1855, the year of the third cholera outbreak of the century. He was still in office at the last terrible epidemic in 1866 which was at its worst in the East End. Staff and resources were strained to the utmost. Patients were nursed on pallets of straw, which were burnt every night. Mr Nixon himself escaped the disease, and served the hospital for many years more.

Francis Carr-Gomm (b) was chairman of the house committee in 1884, the year in which Sir Frederick Treves first saw the tragic Joseph Merrick, the Elephant Man. He later brought him to live in the hospital. Mr Carr-Gomm strongly supported Sir Frederick, and by enlisting the sympathy and financial support of royalty and the public, disarmed the opposition of the house committee to Merrick's admission.

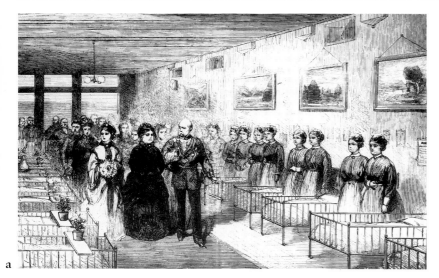

a

b

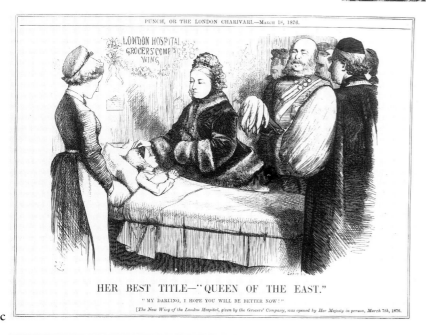

PUNCH, OR THE LONDON CHARIVARI.—MARCH 18, 1876.

HER BEST TITLE—"QUEEN OF THE EAST."

"MY DARLING, I HOPE YOU WILL BE BETTER NOW!"

[The New Wing of the London Hospital, given by the Grocers' Company, was opened by Her Majesty in person, March 7th, 1876.

c

II 3. Queen Victoria's visit

The great event of 1876 was the opening by Queen Victoria of the new Grocers' Wing (a), largely paid for by the Grocers' Company. This was The Queen's first visit to the East End since the death of Prince Albert fifteen years before and enthusiastic crowds welcomed her (b). She also visited the Alexandra Wing, the foundation stone of which had been laid in 1864 by Alexandra, Princess of Wales and her husband (later Edward VII). The child being visited (c) is said to have told the hospital chaplain that she 'was sure she would get well if she could only see the Queen'.

II 4. Sister with scissors

Today's disposable instruments were undreamed of
until after the last war. The Victorian sister carried her
scissors and forceps as securely fastened to her person
as her modern counterpart does the drug-cupboard
keys.

II 5. Miss Lückes as a young woman

Within twenty-four hours of her appointment, Miss Lückes told the house committee that the nursing staff at The London was grossly inadequate both in quality and in numbers. Eighty years later, another young matron, Miss Phyllis Friend, pointed out immediately after her appointment that another hundred nurses were needed.

II 6. Miss Lückes and her assistants

Miss Lückes is seen here with her assistants. Two of them subsequently became matrons of The London. On Miss Lückes' right is Miss Monk who was appointed matron following Miss Lückes' death in 1919. Seated on her extreme left is Miss Littleboy, who took over as matron in 1931 on the retirement of Miss Monk. In this way there was continuity of Miss Lückes' ideas until the arrival of Miss Clare Alexander.

Sydney Holland reading aloud to miss Lückes. June 23, 1912.

II 7/8. Sydney Holland, second Viscount Knutsford

Sydney Holland was elected chairman of The London Hospital in 1896 at the age of 40. Upon his election he began the campaign which led to enormous developments and improvements in the hospital. He worked very closely with Eva Lückes who attached

great value to his work and support. Sydney Holland's energy, initiative and perseverance in raising money (8a) earned him the title of 'The Prince of Beggars'. His most famous effort was made in 1923 when the hospital was heavily in debt. An acquaintance promised to

HON SYDNEY HOLLAND PROPOSES 'THE LORD MAYOR' AND PLEADS THE HOSPITAL CAUSE

a

£50,000   £50,000

b

double any money given by the end of the year, and the eventual grand total was no less than £180,000. He is seen here with the result of the appeal (8b), which he said was 'a beggar's dream'.

His memorial tablet pays tribute to him: 'Through him the Hospital was largely rebuilt and equipped to serve generations to come. Above all, he inspired it in every part with his own spirit and love of service.'

a

II 9. Sir Jonathan Hutchinson, FRS

Jonathan Hutchinson (1828–1913), born into a Quaker family in Yorkshire, became one of the most distinguished and widely known doctors ever to have been elected to the staff of The London. He was an extremely diligent and accurate observer and recorder of clinical information.

The early photographs show him as a young surgeon on the staff (a), and the theatre in which he would have operated (b). He acquired such wide knowledge and authority concerning specialist subjects, that he was described as Europe's greatest general practitioner. He was also a renowned teacher and attracted students from far and wide. He was the first dean of the medical college. He introduced new ideas into teaching, notably the use of museums and the organization of postgraduate education for doctors. He chose these words for his tombstone – 'A Man of hope and forward-looking mind'.

b

a

b

c

II 10. Dr John Hughlings Jackson, FRS – founder of the neurological tradition at The London

Assisted by his life-long friend and fellow Yorkshireman Jonathan Hutchinson, Hughlings Jackson (1835–1911) became physician at The London in 1874 (a). During the next 30 years, 'out of the chaos of isolated and sometimes wild speculations and unrelated experiments, [he] organized and laid the foundation of modern neurology', becoming the greatest neurologist of his time. His name will always be associated with the form of epilepsy caused by a localized cortical disorder, but his contributions were both more general and more fundamental. He established a tradition of world renown in neurology at The London, which was continued by Sir Henry Head FRS (b), a man of brilliance, enthusiasm and originality. Of an earlier generation at The London was Dr John Langdon-Down (1828–1870), whose name will always be associated with Down's Syndrome (c).

II 11. Hookey Alf

'Hookey Alf of Whitechapel' appears in an early photograph from *Street Life of London* by Thompson and Smith, published about 1880*. Alf's arm was crushed in an accident at his work in the London Docks. He was taken to The London Hospital where the arm had to be amputated; his hook would have been supplied by the hospital's Samaritan Society, which provided patients with surgical appliances. As provider for his family, Alf was thereafter obliged to look for casual work in Whitechapel's public houses.

*Reproduced by kind permission of Vestry House Museum (London Borough of Waltham Forest)

II 12. Sir Morell Mackenzie

Morell Mackenzie (1837–1892) was born in Leytonstone, the son of a local surgeon who died from injuries sustained when he fell from his carriage when Morell was a boy. After working in an insurance office Morell studied medicine at The London. Early in his career he visited the continent and learned to use the laryngoscope, recently invented by the Spanish singing master Garcia. Because of his special knowledge and expertise, Morell Mackenzie became the father and founder of British laryngology. Sadly, the last years of his life were overshadowed by intense international controversy and recriminations surrounding the death of the Emperor of Germany. When still Crown Prince, Frederick, who was married to Queen Victoria's eldest daughter, developed laryngeal symptoms; Mackenzie was called in consultation. After taking biopsies, a procedure only recently available, he advised against an operation, which at that time would have been very dangerous. He received unfair blame and calumny when Frederick died some three months after being crowned Emperor.

a

b

II 13. Sir Andrew Clark, FRS, PRCP and Dr Samuel Fenwick

During much of Queen Victoria's reign Sir Andrew Clark (1826–1893) (*a*) and Dr Samuel Fenwick (1821–1902) (*b*) were distinguished physicians at The London. Each had early struggles to obtain a medical education, Clark being apprenticed to a doctor in Scotland when he was 13, and Fenwick starting his apprenticeship at 14. Clark was a fluent speaker, brilliant teacher and elegant writer. He became the leading physician in London and President of the Royal College of Physicians. Fenwick was less well known outside The London, but was an excellent physician who accomplished an immense amount of work. He had a special interest in diseases of the abdomen and would now be called a gastroenterologist – the first at The London.

a

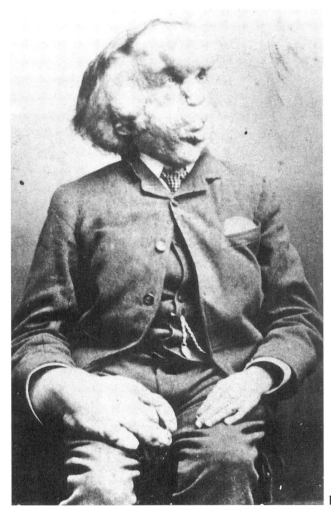

b

II 14. Sir Frederick Treves

The national esteem in which 'Freddie' Treves (1853–1923) (a) was held did much to keep The London in the forefront of public consciousness in the late nineteenth century and the early years of this century. After qualifying from The London he became assistant surgeon at 26 and full member of the consultant staff five years later. His appointment coincided with a time when advances had become possible in surgery of the abdomen, including an understanding of the true nature of appendicitis, a term coined in the USA. Treves made an important contribution to the subject by his advocacy of surgical treatment for this condition. In

1902 his fame became worldwide when he successfully operated on King Edward VII, two days before the date fixed for his coronation. Treves was an eminent anatomist, surgeon, teacher, writer and friend of royalty. In the last of the many books he wrote he gave his account to the general public of the Elephant Man. Many years previously Treves had befriended the deformed and destitute Joseph Merrick (b), and had persuaded the hospital authorities to make an exception to the rules, so that a permanent refuge could be provided in a room off Bedstead Square, near the side entrance to the hospital in East Mount Street.

Dressing a limb

Registering attendance at dinner

Making a patient comfortable

Bringing up dinner

Out door relief

Carving for the patients

A special case

A corner of the Nurses dining room

Preparing bandages

A busy time in the kitchen

Waiting on the Doctor

Sisters afternoon tea

II 15. Composite sketches: picture of life c.1897

Yesterday's desperately ill child, in his steam tent, was 'specialled' in the ward. Today's is whisked off to a high-tech intensive-care unit. One thing remains unchanged: the life of the patient depends on the vigilance of the nurse at the bedside.

MARIE CELESTE HORA.
(NÉE DE VALERIE
Born March 1826.

Married
Christmas Eve
1846.

JAMES HORA. F.R.C.T.
(CITIZEN OF LONDON)
Born July, 1826.

II 16. Benefactors – the Marie Celeste Samaritan Society

The Samaritan Society had been founded in 1791 by Sir William Blizard. More than a century later, in 1898, the society was given a large annual subscription by James Hora in memory of his first wife, Marie Celeste. He felt that he had not taken enough care of her whilst they were living in Australia, where she was very unhappy, and to perpetuate her memory he asked for her name to be associated with the hospital in some way. The title of the society (to which he also left £120,000 in his will) was changed to the Marie Celeste Samaritan Society. James Hora also gave money to endow the Marie Celeste maternity wards.

II 17. The Boer War

Londoners served loyally and with distinction in the Boer War. As soon as the war started the Princess of Wales asked for six London Hospital nurses to be selected for service in South Africa, presenting each at Marlborough House with her own medal and two warm shawls. The six are shown in the group with Miss Lückes and other staff. A year later twenty more nurses were sent out, some of whom died from enteric (typhoid) fever, and several of whom were awarded the Royal Red Cross. Frederick Treves formed his own surgical team which included two sisters from The London, and he later described his experiences in the *Tale of a Field Hospital* (1900).

II 18. Sir Neville Reginald Howse

Sir Neville Reginald Howse, a London Hospital doctor in the New South Wales Medical Staff Corps, was awarded the Victoria Cross for exceptional gallantry. The VC citation from the *London Gazette*, 4 June 1901 (p. 3769), reads: 'During the action at Vredfort on 24th July 1900, Captain House [sic] went out under a heavy cross fire and picked up a wounded man, and carried him to a place of shelter.'

HEBREW WARD LONDON HOSPITAL

II 19. Jewish patients

On behalf of the large Jewish community separate wards were kept for Hebrew patients so that they could observe their own rites. These were endowed by benefactors such as Baron N.M. de Rothschild, E.L. Raphael and A. Goldsmid. Externally these wards had no distinctive features, beyond the small metal slips, mezuzzas, nailed slantwise on the lintels of the door encasing the tables of the law, and passover cake of unleavened bread which, year in, year out, hung on the wall. Hebrew wards did, however, have their own kosher kitchen and separate staff. This deference to the scruples of the orthodox jew made the hospital the only one of its kind at that time.

After the Second World War, the special wards were discontinued, but kosher meals and ceremonies were still provided for, as they are today.

II 20. Tailoring workshop

Here a group of Jewish tailors is seen in their
workshop*. Tailoring and textile manufacture have
been major sources of employment in the East End
since the seventeenth century, with the immigration of

Huguenots from France. Garment making is now
largely in the hands of the Asian community.

*Reproduced by kind permission of the London Museum of Jewish
Life.

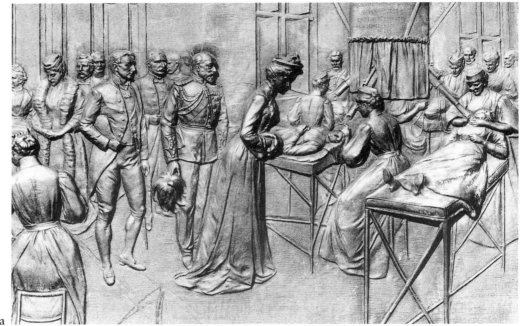

a

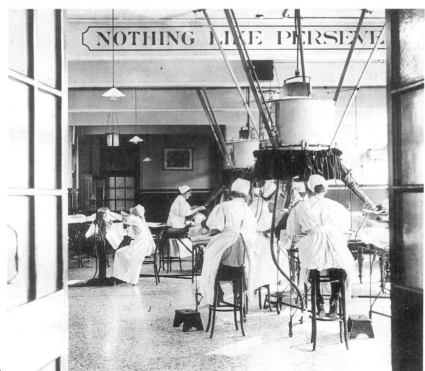

b

II 21. The Finsen Light

The Finsen Light used in the treatment of tuberculosis of the skin (*Lupus vulgaris*), and named after Dr Niels Ryberg Finsen, was brought to The London by Queen Alexandra (*a*). Doctors and nurses from The London were sent to Finsen's clinic in Denmark to learn how to use the apparatus. The picture (*b*) shows sister and staff nurses shining the lamp with its ultra-violet rays on to the affected part of the patient's face.

The light department in the out-patient department also had carbon-arc lamps for sun-ray treatment to the body. Many patients came long distances to the hospital for this type of treatment, and board and lodging arrangements were made for them in the locality through the generosity of the Marie Celeste Samaritan Society.

a

HER MAJESTY
QUEEN ALEXANDRA
PRESIDENT·OF·THE·LONDON·HOSPITAL
1904
WHO·ALWAYS·TOOK·A·PERSONAL·&·SYMPATHETIC·INTEREST·IN·ITS·WORK
AND·WHO·IN·1900·INTRODUCED·TO·ENGLAND
THE·FINSEN·LIGHT·CURE·FOR·LUPUS
AND·PRESENTED·THE·FIRST·LAMP·TO·THIS·HOSPITAL
THIS·STATUE·WAS·ERECTED·BY·FRIENDS·OF·THE·HOSPITAL
1908

b

II 22. Statue of Queen Alexandra

Queen Alexandra's connection with the hospital began when she was Princess of Wales. She became president in 1904. Her statue in bronze was erected in the garden in 1907 (*a*) and has sometimes been embellished with unusual decorations! It is one of only two of her known to exist, the other being in her native Denmark. The inscription (*b*) commemorates aspects of her work for the hospital, which she visited frequently, both formally and informally. The statue is a focal point in the hospital today and a favoured meeting place.

a

b

II 23. Nurse training and education at The London

Miss Swift, appointed Matron in 1867, brought many of the ideas of Florence Nightingale to The London and in 1873 the governors established a Nurse Training School. Probationers at this time signed on for three years and served a further year as trained nurses. Only after Miss Lückes became Matron in 1880, however, did any formal teaching begin. The training was reduced to two years with lectures from Matron and the medical staff, and classes from ward sisters. Subjects covered were elementary physiology and medical nursing; elementary anatomy and surgical nursing.

Lectures and classes (a) were given at 8.00 pm so that day and night probationers could attend. In 1895 the Preliminary Training School was opened at Tredegar House – the first in the country. In 1901 new classrooms, a cookery kitchen (b) and a cloakroom were built.

a

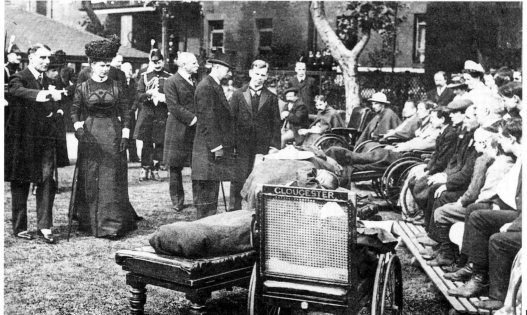

b

II 24. Royal connections

Queen Alexandra (*a*) remained the hospital's president until her death in 1925, when Queen Mary accepted the presidency. Queen Mary visited the Hospital with George V (*b*) soon after his accession in 1910. During his serious illness, in 1928, the King was nursed by staff from The London.

Viscount Knutsford is seen at the side of both Queens in these pictures.

II 25. The receiving room

For many people in the East End at this time a visit to
the doctor meant a long wait in the receiving room of
The London Hospital. Known to staff and regulars as
the 'R.R.', this area was always busy and crowded.

II 26. Mothers and babies

These mothers and babies (including two with twins) often went home to dreadful housing conditions. Whole families might live, eat, work and sleep in one room. Infectious diseases such as diphtheria, epidemic diarrhoea and vomiting in babies, typhoid and tuberculosis were rife. All could be linked directly to the overcrowding and insanitary conditions in which many East Enders lived at that time.

II 27. Dame Rosalind Paget

Dame Rosalind, a great leader of the nursing profession, was a founder member of the National Institute of Midwifery. She worked hard to ensure that midwives were part of a fully trained and respected profession. She is seen here in the dress uniform of a London Hospital Sister.

At the end of the last century, massage – the forerunner of modern physiotherapy – was carried out by nursing sisters who were largely untrained in the art. Rosalind Paget, herself trained in massage, played a major part in the establishment of physiotherapy as a profession. She was a member of The Incorporated Society of Trained Masseuses which became in 1942 The Chartered Society of Physiotherapists.

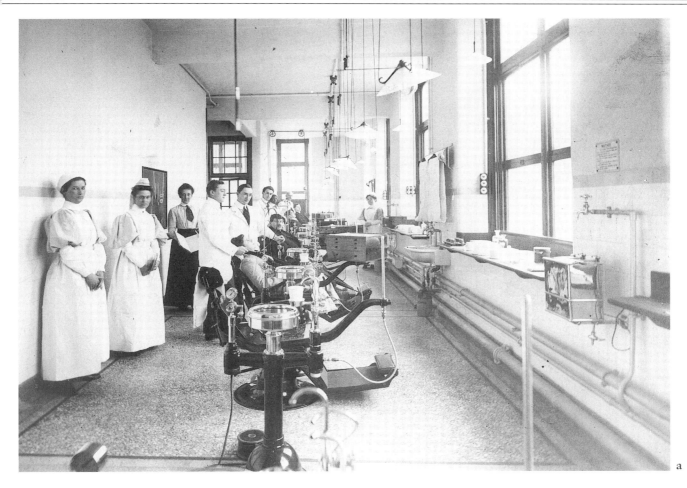

a

II 28. Dental School

This view of the main dental clinic (*a*), the conservation room, must have been taken very shortly after the opening of the dental school in 1911. It gives an impression of being a record of the staff – the figures are hardly plausible as students, and the most distant figure is undoubtedly Francis Farmer. It was Francis Farmer (*b*) who first proposed that a dental school should be formed and he was a founder member of staff. The foot treadle engines which powered the drills can be seen. The room remained in use for this purpose – though with many changes in equipment and lay-out – until 1965. In the twenties, when there were 110 students, it was so crowded that it was difficult to move between the chairs.

b

a

II 29. Professor William Bulloch, FRS and the contributions of specialists

Medical teaching was reorganized at The London at the end of the nineteenth century by the surgeon, H.P. Dean (1864–1931), who encouraged the participation of specialists. Three men who were appointed to the medical college at this time became leaders in their subjects: Sir Leonard Hill, FRS (1866–1952), physiologist; Sir Arthur Keith, FRS (1866–1955), anatomist; and Professor William Bulloch, FRS (1868–1942), bacteriologist.

Bulloch was The London's first bacteriologist, specializing in a subject which had recently been advanced dramatically by the work of Louis Pasteur, Robert Koch and Paul Ehrlich, in France and Germany. Bulloch had been a pupil of Koch and was a friend of Ehrlich. As a result The London was the first hospital in the country in which the drug salvarsan was used for treating syphilis, marking the beginning of a new era of therapeutic success in bacterial diseases. Bulloch was both scholarly and stimulating, with a reputation as a raconteur and mimic. In his neat hand he compiled a biographical record of past doctors at The London – Bulloch's Roll, now a valuable item in the hospital archives.

II 30. Sir James Mackenzie and advances in cardiology

James Mackenzie (1853–1925) (a) was the son of a farmer in Scotland who, after serving a six-year apprenticeship with a chemist, studied medicine in Edinburgh. He then spent nearly 28 years in general practice in Burnley. While working as a general practitioner he made observations on the behaviour and rhythm of the heart in health and disease, which made him world-famous. For these studies he used various mechanical devices, including the polygraph illustrated here (b). He was persuaded to come to The London first to do research, and then as the founder and first head of the cardiac department (c). It was in the Department of Anatomy of the medical college that the natural pacemaking system which controls the heartbeat was discovered by Martin Flack and Sir Arthur Keith. The fruits of their work are evident today in the development of the artificial pacemaker to which many people owe their lives.

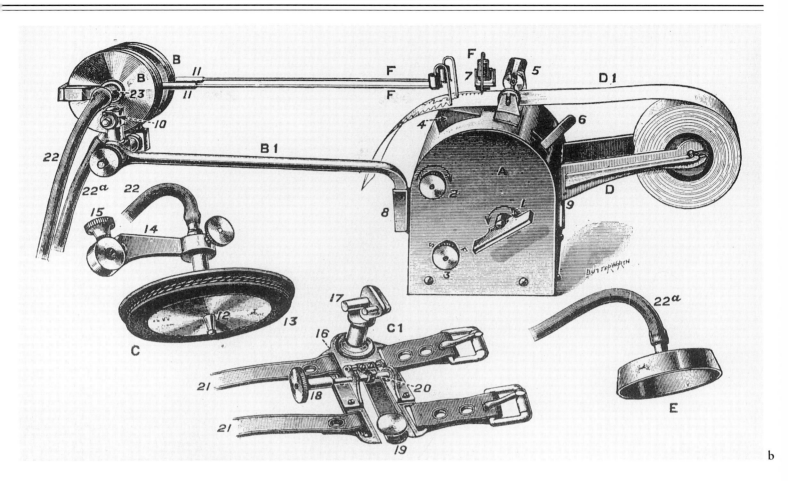

b

AS A MEMORIAL TO
THE WORK OF SIR JAMES MACKENZIE M.D., F.R.S
THE SUM OF £4,321 WAS COLLECTED
TOWARDS THE COST OF THIS BUILDING BY
THE GENERAL EAST-END TRADESMEN'S ASSOCIATION

PRESIDENTS { ARTHUR RAYMENT   HON. TREASURER F.G.COCKERILL
           { WILLIAM HARVEY   HON. SECRETARY G. LEADBEATER
VICE-PRESIDENT P. W. BROWN   ASST. HON. SECRETARY P. ARTER

THIS CARDIAC DEPARTMENT WAS OPENED BY
Mʀs CECIL E.W. CHARRINGTON
25 NOVEMBER 1931.

c

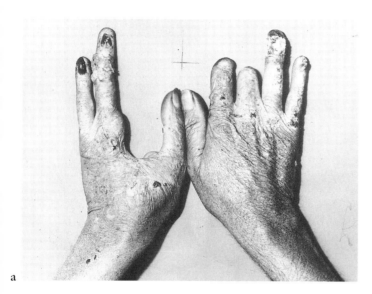

a

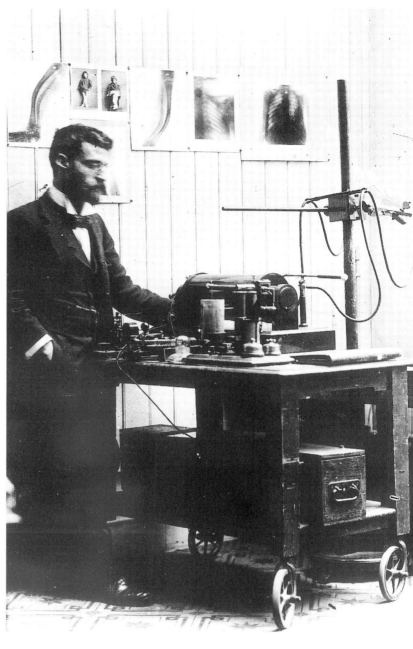

IN PROUD MEMORY
OF
REGINALD BLACKALL · HAROLD SUGGARS
ERNEST HARNACK · ERNEST WILSON
1896 – 1943
THESE FOUR FRIENDS, AS PIONEER RADIOGRAPHERS
DEVOTED THEIR LIVES TO HEALING
THEIR WORK IN THE DEVELOPMENT OF THE
SCIENCE OF X-RAYS
COST THEM THEIR HEALTH
THIS THEY GLADLY GAVE IN THE SERVICE OF
THE LONDON HOSPITAL

c

II 31. X-ray martyrs

The London was one of the first hospitals in the country to make use of X-rays in diagnosis. Soon after Röntgen discovered his rays in 1895, an advertisement was placed for a doctor to take charge of an 'electrical department'. The hospital was still lit by gas rather than electricity, so that an accumulator, which needed recharging at the People's Palace nearby, was used. To begin with, the danger of repeated exposure, causing X-ray burns (a) and sometimes cancer, was not appreciated. Sadly, The London claimed four amongst 100 recorded X-ray martyrs in the world. In the illustration (b), Dr Hedley, a member of the department, stands next to a primitive X-ray machine. In 1943 a plaque (c) was unveiled in the hospital in memory of The London's X-ray martyrs.

a

"WAIFS AND STRAYS."

b

II 32. Dr Thomas Barnardo

Dr Hudson Taylor, who qualified at The London and then took both the Gospel and his medical skills to China, was the first of many London Hospital missionaries. It was when young Tom Barnardo (a) attended one of Hudson Taylor's revivalist meetings that he was inspired to follow his example. At an early stage in his training at The London, there was a serious outbreak of cholera. The consequences for the inhabitants of the East End, and particularly the plight of children, so moved him that he decided to devote the rest of his life to orphans and destitute children (b). He is remembered for his establishment of children's homes and refuges which are still in operation now. Outside the house in Stepney was the notice: 'No destitute child ever refused admittance.'

II 33. Grenfell of Labrador (opposite)

As a medical student at The London, Wilfred Grenfell (*a*) (1865–1940) was both an excellent sportsman and a deeply committed christian. He taught at a local Sunday School where he displayed all the attributes of the 'muscular christianity' that Charles Kingsley, author of *The Water Babies*, had made popular. He was influenced in the exercise of his christianity by Sir Frederick Treves and the year after he qualified as a doctor he became a medical missionary. This was a vocation which many of The London's students followed at the time, particularly in the Far East.

For five years Grenfell practised as a medical missionary to deep-sea fishermen from Iceland (*b*) to the Bay of Biscay; he then started a medical mission in Labrador (*c + d*), which was to become his life's work, and continues today.

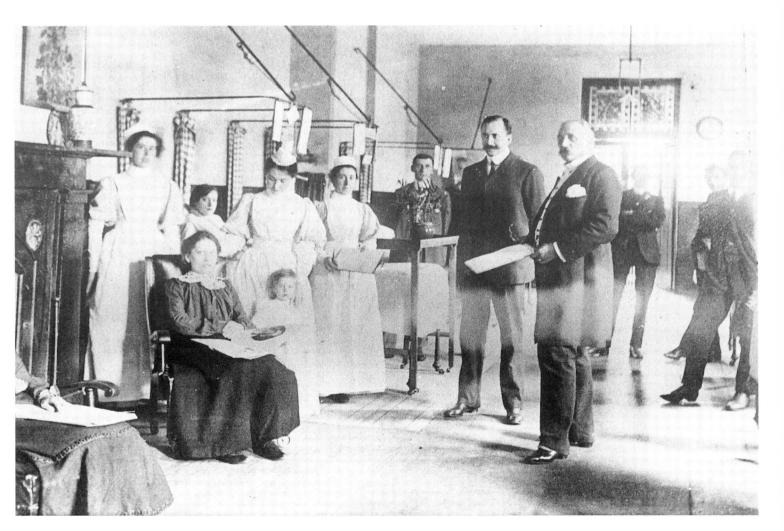

II 34. Doctor's round in frock coat

In the early part of the twentieth century the frock coat was standard wear for professional men, and doctors were no exception. The 'chief's' round was an important event. Tall consultants tended to hang on to the bedrails while teaching, so the most junior probationer's contribution was to wash the curtain rails of the beds of the 'chief's' patients just before he came.

a

b

II 35. The First World War

Nurses joining the armed forces were issued with standard camping equipment. The nurse shown here (a) found the nurses' garden a good place to learn the uses of all her new property. Note the stove, lamp and canvas bucket as well as bed, chair and washing bowl. The garden of the main hospital was used as a practice-ground for erecting tents (b).

II 36. Wounded

The first wounded soldiers arrived at The London from France as early as 30 August 1914 (*a*). The hospital was asked to take them at very short notice, and no ambulances were available. Within an hour, the chairman of the caterers, J. Lyons & Co., who was a member of the house committee, had arranged for fourteen vans to convey the men to Whitechapel.

Amongst the casualties in the very early months of the war were 200 Belgian soldiers whose country had already been overrun by the German army.

Officers as well as 'Tommies' were nursed in the hospital (*b*), but only the officers had eiderdowns for their beds. On each floor a section was cleared for use as a games/sitting room.

a

b

II 37. Edith Cavell

Miss Edith Cavell was born at Swardeston, near Norwich, where her father was rector, on 4 December 1865. At school Edith showed a particular interest in learning French, and as a result took up a position as governess to the family of a lawyer in Brussels. She returned home after several years to look after her father, who was seriously ill. This experience led her to train as a nurse at The London and subsequently to move to Brussels (a). In 1907, Edith Cavell was invited to establish a training school there on similar lines to the Florence Nightingale School. In the initial stages of the First World War she was instrumental in helping wounded soldiers to escape back to the Allied lines. As a result she was arrested on 5 August 1915 and was executed by the German army.

A plaque in memory of her (b) on the wall of one of the nurses' homes was unveiled in 1989.

a

b

II 38. Edith Cavell's statues

Before she died Edith Cavell wrote to Brand Whitlock, the American representative in Brussels: 'I have seen death so often that it is not fearful or strange to me, and this I would say, standing in view of God and eternity, I realise that patriotism is not enough; I must have no hatred or bitterness against anyone.'

She is commemorated by statues in her honour both in Brussels (a) and in London (b). Every year two London Hospital Sisters in uniform lay a laurel wreath at the statue in London, which is situated at the bottom of St Martin's Lane.

II 39. Sister's sitting room

The room adjoining the ward was Sister's private sitting room, her home, possibly for twenty years. Provided with basic furniture only, each decorated it to her own taste. This was the only place where she could relax, or entertain her friends, where she ate her meals and spent endless hours on duty call. Only in the 1940s, when non-residence became acceptable, did Sister's sitting room become her office.

II 40. Grannie Collyer

Wardmaids were local women who often remained for many years in the same ward. Like the nurses, they worked split duties, returning from a free afternoon for an evening shift. To the ward sister, her wardmaid was invaluable. One or two were terrifying, but most are remembered with gratitude by the nurses whom they mothered or shielded from the stern arm of the law – Sister.

Nurses Garden London Hospital

II 41. The Garden of Eden

The nurses' garden, the Garden of Eden, was established by Miss Lückes for the relaxation of her staff. It was furnished with hammocks, cushions, even a penny-in-the-slot meter for boiling water, and the porter on duty at the back gate lodge unlocked it for the staff. It was redesigned in the 1930s when the nurses' swimming pool was built.

III · Change and Challenge:
1919–1947

a

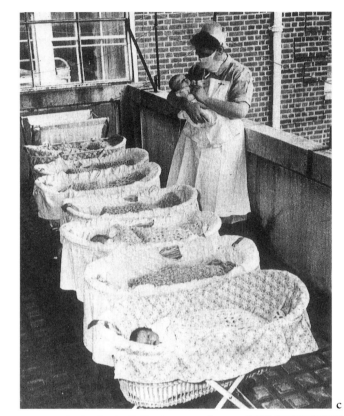

c

b

III 1. Queen Mary opens 'her' maternity home (opposite)

This photograph of Queen Mary and the Princess Royal (*a*) was taken at the opening of Queen Mary's Maternity Home, Hampstead (*b*). The home was built on the site of a fashionable Georgian inn, headquarters of the Kitkat Club, a renowned social and literary club. The grounds were purchased by Queen Mary in 1916 and the home purpose-built to provide the best possible facilities for maternity care. Queen Mary and her ladies-in-waiting crocheted all the cot blankets (*c*). The home was subsequently linked with The London for midwifery training and the joining of 'her two hospitals' was a great source of satisfaction to the Queen.

III 2. On her rounds of The London

Queen Mary became president of The London in 1924. Her Majesty was interested in everything and thoroughly inspected the hospital – even to opening the cupboard doors, to the great worry of the staff, as she toured round. She continued to be interested in children. Matron, Miss Littleboy, wrote in 1936: 'At the request of Her Majesty, Queen Mary, the Paragon China people wrote asking how many children we should have in the wards for Christmas, as Her Majesty wished to send each child a mug, and we asked for eighty-four. You can imagine how delighted we were with this gift, especially as the mugs were inscribed on the bottom with the following words "A gift from Her Majesty, Queen Mary, 1936" and were very daintily decorated with nursery rhymes and pictures.'

a

b

III 3. Children need sunlight

The need for sunlight, good food and fresh air (*a* + *b*) was paramount to combat rickets, respiratory diseases and poor nutrition. In 1922, Ernest Morris, house governor, accompanied a district midwife on her visits and described some of the conditions they saw. 'The room was empty except for three or four absolute necessities . . . the pile of pawn tickets was on the mantlepiece. . . . Mother had had to pawn the babies' clothes. There were no toys or picture books. Her husband worked in the docks if he was lucky and today there was great jubilation because he had got work.'

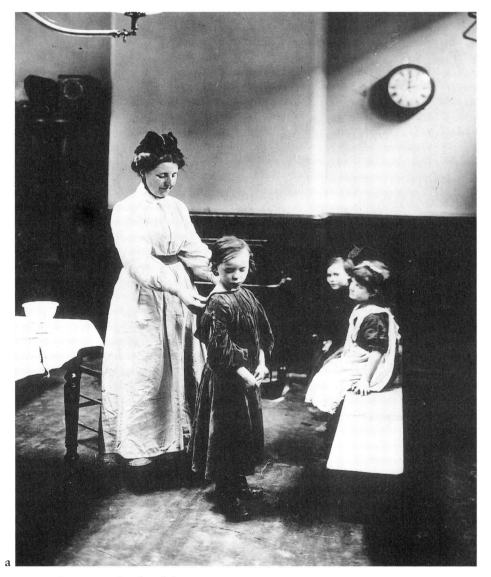

III 4. Community health

The concept of health promotion and preventive medicine led to inspection of children in the community (*a*). 'Penny-a-month helpers League – patients find easy way to help the Hospital they love' was a headline in *The London Hospital Illustrated* in 1936. A possibly unique form of hospital art was created that year for The London Hospital Helpers' League in the form of a silver-coloured metal token. The token portrayed

Hygieia, goddess of health (*b* + *c*). It was claimed that as a result of the token, East Enders were rapidly becoming health-conscious. Each patient who felt he would like to become a member paid a shilling to the Helpers' League office and received his membership token in exchange. Patients were urged to carry them with them at all times.

'ANGELS OF THE POOR' IN EAST END
Friends Of The Mother And Baby

All the anxieties of the East End mother are allayed when the "Green Nurse" from the London Hospital calls on her daily rounds. The tiny mites of the slums grow strong under her guardianship. Read more about the work of these "Angels of the Poor" on page 5.

"Green Nurses" attend maternity cases at the poorest homes within a mile radius of the London Hospital, and they are beloved and trusted by every East-ender.

Here is the Maternity Sister at the London Hospital sending off her outside staff for the day. The familiar green uniform is held in such high esteem in the East End that its wearers can pass safely in the meanest quarters at any hour of the day or night. Some interesting stories of chivalrous Cockney actions, inspired by gratitude for the wonderful service of these nurses, are related in an article elsewhere in this issue. They help to explain why Londoners love "The London," and why this great voluntary Hospital merits your sympathetic support.

III 5. Communications

Started in the 1930s, *The London Hospital Illustrated* built on the considerable foundation of good public relations and genius for communication shown by Viscount Knutsford. It was important not only for publicizing the work of the hospital, raising awareness of its needs, but also for boosting staff morale.

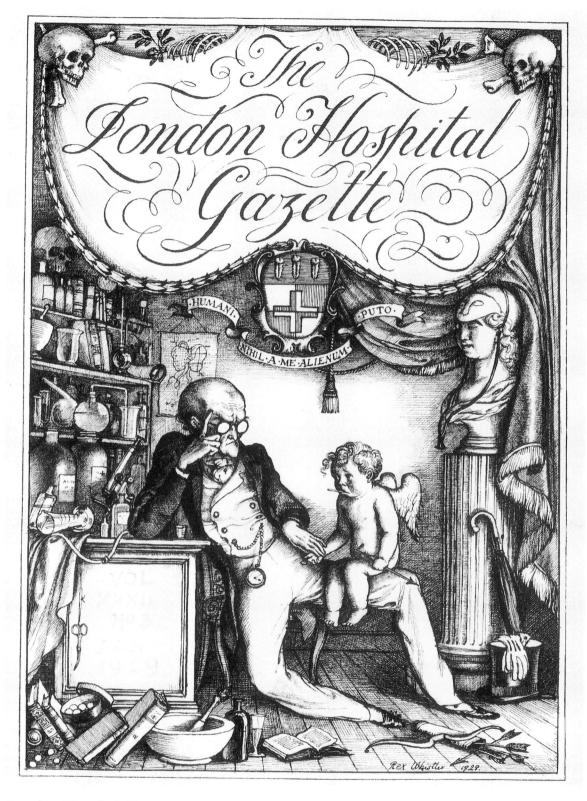

III 6. The London Hospital Gazette

Originally produced by the medical students, now by the Medical and Dental Club, *The London Hospital Gazette* is the means of keeping 'Old Londoners' in touch. The cover shown here was designed by Rex Whistler in 1929.

a

b

III 7. The Good Samaritans

Amongst the largest enterprises in the East End were the breweries – several of which were in Quaker hands. They were noted for brewing fine beer, good treatment of their men, their splendid horses and their generosity to good causes. Seen above (*a*) is the aptly named The Good Samaritan, a Truman house frequented by medical students. The Truman, Hanbury and Buxton families were benefactors, each having wards named after them.

The Charrington horses* seen here (*b*) belong to another brewery linked with another distinguished benefactor. Nearby is the Mann Crossman and Paulin brewery whose chairman, Sir John Mann, took over as Chairman of The London in 1943.

*Reproduced by kind permission of Charrington's Brewery, Whitechapel

a

duly sent in the guinea with the following statement of account :

1920	£	s.	d.
July 17—Putting rubber heels on shoes..			3
,, 20—Mending dusting brush			6
,, 21— ,, flat iron			3
,, 23—Tickets for bazaar (making)		1	0
,, 27— ,, ,, raffle			6
Aug. 20—Violets sold			3
,, 20—Love offering		3	3
,, 21—Riveting pair of braces			3
Oct. 4—Restringing zither harp		1	0
,, 5—Mending umbrella handle.......			3
,, 6— ,, ash pan			3
,, 6—Writing two window tickets		1	0
,, 8—Putting in pane of glass			6
,, 8—Making window screen		2	6
,, 23—Violets			6
,, 23— ,, ...			6
,, 23—Putting rubbers on heels			3
,, 23—Sold to various people grapes grown on coal shed		6	6
,, 23—Love offering		1	0
,, 25—Sold a kitten			6
,, 30— ,, a " Pears Annual " picture			6
	1	1	0

b

HALF·A·CROWN
will run all this for
HALF·A·MINUTE

QUINQUENNIAL APPEAL
for
TWO MILLION HALF-CROWNS

HALF·A·CROWN
will run all this for
HALF·A·MINUTE

c

III 8. Raising the much-needed money

The Knutsford clock collection box seen here (a) dates from before the First World War but it and countless others could be found during the 1920s and '30s in private homes and on nearly every railway station in London.

Other ingenious Knutsford devices included the collecting umbrella, the fountain-pen gamble, the forget-me-not bond, and the milk churn – the last filled to pay the hospital's milk bill.

Seen here also is an account of how a grateful but impoverished patient worked to earn a guinea for the hospital appeal (b).

The quinquennial appeal for two million half-crowns (c) was yet another ploy devised by 'the Prince of Beggars' (Lord Knutsford), raising much-needed cash.

III 9. An unexpected act of generosity

During King George V's jubilee celebrations, as London Hospital nurses were selling programmes to seatholders in the stands, Mr Edward Meyerstein saw them and decided he would offer money for their recreation. The gift of a swimming bath for the nurses was the direct outcome. It was built on part of the garden – the Garden of Eden. One of the big events was the annual gala, culminating in a topical fancy dress competition.

III 10. Ward names

Each of the wards at The London bears the name of a person or a family from whose generosity the hospital has benefited.

Such a benefactor was Charles Cotes, a member of the house committee who started a fund in his newspaper, *The Sun*, to raise money to purchase feather pillows. These replaced the old flock ones, and on the last Christmas of the nineteenth century the head of every patient rested on a feather pillow.

LIST OF WARDS.—1927.

Ward.	Sub-Ward.	Remarks—Cause of Naming, &c.	Date.
Ada Lewis (Female Ophthalmic Ward).		A Legacy of £20,000 was left by Samuel Lewis, reversionary upon the death of his wife, Ada Lewis, to name a Ward in memory of her	1907
Blizard		Sir William Blizard, the eminent Surgeon.	1876
	Pelly	Sir J. H. Pelly, Bart., V.P., and Captain Richard W. Pelly, R.N., V.P. (Father and Son)	
Buxton (Children's Ward).		Thomas Fowell Buxton.—Treasurer	1870
Cambridge		In honour of the President—Adolphus Frederick, Duke of Cambridge	1835
	Albert	In honour of H.R.H. Prince Albert	1842
Charles Cotes		Member of the House-Committee, in grateful remembrance of his earnest work	1903
	William IV.	By His Majesty's permission	1832
Charrington		A family of eminent supporters of the Hospital	1876
	Davis	William and John Davis, V.P's. (Father and Son), active and liberal supporters of the Hospital	1870
Cotton		In memory of Wm. Cotton, V.P.	1870
	Fraser	In memory of Dr. Patrick Fraser, Assistant Physician, January, 1845; Physician, February, 1853; and in recognition of the generosity of his Widow, Martha Maria Fraser	1903
Crossman		Robert Crossman and James Hiscutt Crossman (Father and Son), Members of House-Committee (Father	1876
			1876
			1876
			1903
			1832
			1832
			1773
			1923
			1750

LIST OF WARDS (continued).

Ward.	Sub-Ward	Remarks—Cause of Naming, &c.	Date.
Grocers		A Donation of £10,000 from the Worshipful Company of Grocers	1915
Gurney		Samuel Gurney, V.P., and Samuel Gurney (son of the former), also V.P.	1870
	Barclay	Joseph Gurney Barclay, V.P.	1870
Hanbury		Robert Hanbury, V.P., and Osgood Hanbury, V.P.	1870
	Young	George Frederick Young, Chairman, House-Committee, and Frederick Young, Member of House-Committee	1870
Harrison		John Harrison.—Founder of the Hospital	1740
	Fitzgerald	Keane Fitzgerald.—Left by Will to this Institution £10,000	1831
Helene Raphael (Hebrew Ward).		Endowed by the late E. L. Raphael in 1899, in memory of his wife. Opened in 1904.	
	Goldsmid	In memory of Abraham Goldsmid.—A liberal benefactor of the Hospital	1870
Marie Celeste (Maternity Wards).		In memory of the wife of James Hora, V.P.—a munificent benefactor to the Hospital, who gave a large sum towards the Endowment of these Wards	1900
Mary		A tribute of respect to the Duchess of Gloucester	1771
	Maude Ashley	In consideration of gifts of War Stock from Sir Ernest Cassel, G.C.B., G.C.M.G., G.C.V.O.	1916
Mary Northcliffe		Named after the Viscountess Northcliffe, a generous supporter of the Hospital	1920
Mellish		A family of continuous early supporters	1778
	Treves	After Sir Frederick Treves, Bart., G.C.V.O., C.B., LL.D., Serjeant-Surgeon to H.M. King Edward VII.	
Milward		In memory of John Milward's Legacy—(about) £26,000	1831
	Annie Zunz	A Donation of £10,000—From the Trustees of the Will of the late Siegfried Rudolf Zunz	1908
Ophthalmic Wards		Known as Male Ophthalmic Ward. No specific name.	
Paulin		In recognition of the many years of devoted service given to the Hospital by William Thomas Paulin. Elected Life Governor 1857; Member of House-Committee 1895, and Treasurer 1913	1921
	Adelaide	By Her Majesty's gracious permission	1831
Princess Beatrice (Children's Ward).		Named by Her Majesty Queen Victoria, March	1870

LIST OF WARDS (continued).

Ward.	Sub-Ward.	Remarks—Cause of Naming, &c.	Date.
Queen Victoria (Children's Ward).		Named by Her Majesty Queen Victoria, March	1876
Rachel		After the late Mrs. T. Fowell Buxton	1876
	Emily	Mrs. Octavius E. Coope	1876
Rothschild (Hebrew Ward).		In memory of Baron N. M. de Rothschild.—A liberal supporter of the Hospital	1870
	Unnamed Hebrew Ward		
Rowsell		Rev. T. J. Rowsell.—Deputy Chairman House-Committee	1876
	Johnston	Andrew Johnston.—House-Committee, 1876.	1891
Royal (Princess)		In honour of Her Royal Highness (married to Crown Prince of Germany)	1842
	Augusta	In honour of the Duchess of Cambridge—Mother of George William, late Duke of Cambridge, President 1850	1842
Sophia		A tribute of respect to the Princess of Gloucester	*Not traceable.*
	Granby	Marquis of Granby.—An early supporter	1778
Talbot		Earl Talbot.—An early benefactor. The four Wards of the Block were restored in memory of his direct lineal descendant and eventual heir, Edward Rhys Wingfield, who died March 14th, 1901	1773
	Gore	One of the first and most zealous supporters of the Charity	1773
Turner		Charles Hampden Turner.—Chairman House-Committee in 1807 (when the first great Collection was made to avert closing Hospital)	1807
	Edward VII.	So named in commemoration of the opening of the Out-Patient Department by His Majesty on June 13th, 1903	1903
	General East End Tradesmen	Contributions from the General East End Tradesmen's Association	1919
	Mayer	In memory of Baron Mayer de Rothschild	1876
Wellington		In honour of the Duke of Wellington, V.P.	1842
	Prince of Wales	In honour of H.R.H.	1842
Yarrow		Sir A. Yarrow, Bart., who defrayed a large part of the cost of the Out-Patient Department	1905
	Helen Croft	In recognition of Mrs. Helen Croft's many generous acts	1915

In the Isolation Block are Wards for Patients suffering from Scarlet Fever, Measles, Diphtheria, etc. One of the Wards in this Block is named "Whiting," in memory of Matthew Whiting, a generous benefactor under his Will—1902.

In addition to the above-named Wards, there are 6 Rooms for "24 hour" cases, 6 for violent cases, 3 for Residents, and Nurses' Sick Rooms with 11 beds. In addition to these there are 18 beds in the Sisters' Rooms.

a

b

III 11. Using the money

Money collected by successive appeals allowed new methods of treatment to be introduced in the 1930s – ultra-violet light, X-rays, short waves and Grenz rays. The former dental department shown here was converted into a light-treatment clinic, where children were given 'sunlight' treatment (a).

At the same time mothers of large families who would not otherwise have been able to relax were transported to the country by ambulance for a convalescent holiday. Croft Home, Reigate, pictured here (b) was opened in 1920. It was rewarding to the staff to see the transformation of care-worn mothers, arriving with pale faces and leaving looking healthy, relaxed and very jolly.

III 12. Looking after the staff

The works outing must have been an important annual occasion for the craftsmen and apprentices. They are seen here setting off from Bedstead Square, by the old Works Department, for a day in Cheddar Gorge. Several generations of a family often worked for the same department.

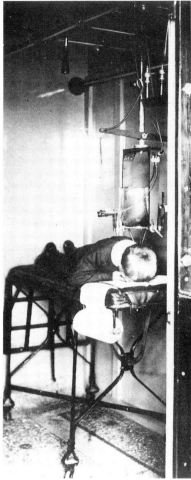

a

b

III 13. New developments

A gramme of radium was given to the hospital by the Medical Research Council in 1935; radon was then prepared from it and used in treatment of certain kinds of cancer. X-rays were used for treatment and diagnosis (*a*).

During the Second World War radium was put down bore holes, in the interests of safety. In 1939, The London's radium was transferred to a disused lime kiln tunnel in a quarry near Barton-in-the-Clay in Bedfordshire. The tunnel was lined, illuminated and ventilated, and a purification plant was set up. Radon gas was extracted from the radium, put into glass capillaries and inserted into platinum sheaths to form 'seeds' or 'needles' for clinical use.

During the First World War, catgut was in short supply due to problems of transport, and a theatre assistant, Mr Morley, started to manufacture it at The London. The ligature department (*b*) originally in the basement of Fielden Block, led in 1922 to the formation of a limited company, all shares held by the hospital. It subsequently moved to larger premises, and the manufacture of London Hospital Catgut (strictly speaking lamb's gut) on a commercial scale brought in considerable annual revenue to the free funds of the hospital.

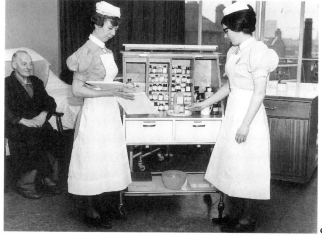

e

c

d

III 14. The pharmacy

Since the days of Josiah Cole, apothecary and founder member of The London, the pharmacy has always had an important role (a). Some of the drugs used were manufactured at the hospital from plants grown in the herb garden – for example foxgloves were used for producing digitalis. Pills were made using early hand machines, and these together with other in-house products were sold to various hospitals (b + c). The Professor of Pharmacology, W.A.M. Smart, taught the medical students how to make pills. Leeches were used for blood-letting and to relieve pain in pleurisy. Skill in the application of these was noted in each nurse's 'white book'. In addition, the hospital had its own pharmacopoeia, and one of its most respected chief pharmacists, Charles Sykes, is pictured here (d). In his time as a student his examination included a test of his ability to decipher doctors' handwriting. He and his staff were later to pioneer new methods of recording and administering drugs in the wards (e). The importance of quality control and income generation was still paramount.

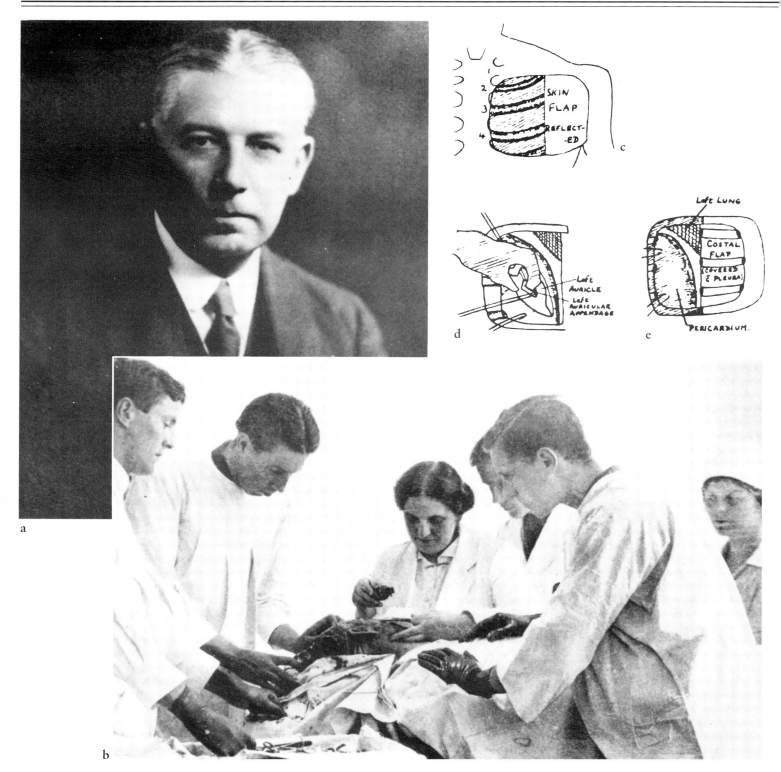

III 15. Sir Henry Souttar – surgical genius

Henry Souttar (1875–1964) was a brilliant and versatile surgeon (a). In 1925 at The London, he became the first surgeon to open a chamber of the heart, the left auricle, in order to stretch the mitral valve. This operation did not become the standard procedure for treatment of severe mitral stenosis (narrowing of the valve), a common complication of rheumatic fever, for another twenty years. The illustrations show Souttar operating (b), together with sketches (c, d + e) drawn of the original operation to explore the mitral valve of a girl of 15.

III 16. Professor Sir Hugh Cairns – pioneer in modern neurosurgery

Hugh Cairns (1896–1953), an Australian Rhodes scholar, came to The London from Oxford as a clinical student. Henry Souttar, when Cairns was his house surgeon, inspired in him an interest in brain surgery. After working with Harvey Cushing in Boston, Massachusetts, Cairns returned to The London and achieved his ambition to be the first head of the new neurosurgical unit at The London. He went on to become one of the pioneers of modern neurosurgery in Britain and established a reputation for excellence in the subject maintained by Douglas Northfield and his successors.

From inability to let well alone;
From too much zeal for the new
and contempt for what is old;
from putting knowledge before wisdom,
science before art, and cleverness before
✠ ✠ ✠ ✠ ✠ common sense, ✠ ✠ ✠ ✠ ✠
from treating patients as cases, and from
making the cure of the disease more
grievous than the endurance of the same,
Good Lord, deliver us."

III 17. Sir Robert Hutchison – physicianly wisdom

Robert Hutchison (1871–1960) was an Edinburgh graduate who was appointed as a young man to the staff of The London Hospital. He was wise and kindly as a physician and paediatrician, was sparing but elegant in his use of language, and conveyed profound truths in his teaching. A verse from his medical 'litany' is shown above his portrait by Sir James Gunn.

III 18. Physicians and nurses to royalty (opposite)

The reputation of Bertrand Edward Dawson (a)*, Viscount Dawson of Penn (1864–1945), rests upon his qualities both as a physician and as a medical statesman. He had a remarkable clinical memory and a profound understanding of men and women, with an ability to inspire trust in those of diverse temperaments and occupations. Though he was physician and trusted friend of the King, he never faltered in his loyalty to The London and to his patients in the East End. In more recent times, Dr Horace Evans (b), Baron Evans of Merthyr Tydfil (1903–1963) also combined remarkable clinical acumen with great charm. He too was physician to royalty and to countless patients in the East End, as well as to the nurses at The London. Shown here (c) also is Sister Miss Catherine Black who nursed George V during his illness in 1928 and was subsequently awarded the MBE and the Royal Red Cross.

*Reproduced by kind permission of the National Portrait Gallery.

c

a

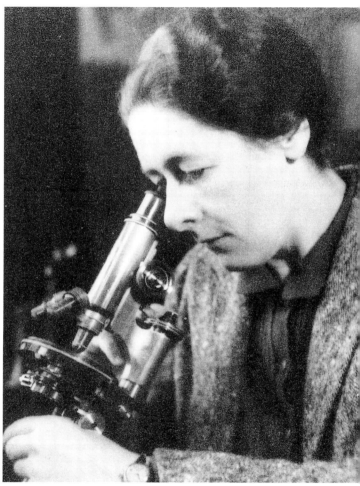

III 19. Professor Hubert Turnbull, FRS and Professor Dorothy Russell – scholars and leaders in pathology

Hubert Turnbull (1875–1955) came to The London as a clinical student, and spent over 40 years as director of the institute of pathology (*a*). He was scholarly and ascetic, with a passion for truth, and he insisted on meticulous standards of observation and recording. Those who worked with him, including many from abroad, were inspired to emulate his methods and standards.

Dorothy Russell (*b*) (1895–1983) was attracted to

pathology by the influence and example of Hubert Turnbull. She became his successor, gaining for herself world renown in the subject of neuropathology. At The London her influence as a teacher was profound, and she set very high standards of intellect and performance. Her achievements also contributed considerably to the advancement of women in British medicine.

III 20. Samuel Bedson, FRS and colleagues – research on bacteria and viruses

From the mid-1920s research at The London was particularly productive. Special funds had been collected to sponsor research, including a large anonymous donation given in 1925 to provide grants for three full-time Freedom fellows. Samuel Bedson (1886–1969) came to The London as a Freedom fellow as did Howard Florey, later Lord Florey, who played a central part in the discovery of the chemotherapeutic properties of penicillin. Samuel Bedson succeeded William Bulloch as Professor of Bacteriology and became a pioneer in the new science of virology. He also successfully isolated the causal agent of psittacosis, both from patients who were being investigated at The London and from infected parrots. Other notable investigators included James McIntosh and Paul Fildes who studied bacteria causing tetanus and gas gangrene. McIntosh and Fildes' jars for culturing such organisms are still in use.

III 21. Evelyn Sprawson – eminent scientist and founder member of the dental school

Professor Evelyn Charles Sprawson, MC, FDS, was a founder member of the staff and, from 1919 until his retirement in 1946, was director of dental studies. In addition to the important and lasting influence he exerted on the school, his research work covered many fields and his eminence as a scientist was recognized by many awards including a Hunterian Professorship of the Royal College of Surgeons. His appointment as dental surgeon to Dr Barnardo's Homes, which he held from 1908 to 1953, gave scope not only to the essential kindliness of his nature but also to his scientific inquisitiveness, for he there carried out important studies on dental caries in children. He was a patient teacher and earned great affection and respect from his associates and students, who presented to him the portrait which is reproduced here. The school itself has recognized its debt by the establishment of the annual Evelyn Sprawson Memorial Lecture and the Evelyn Sprawson prize awarded to Old Londoners.

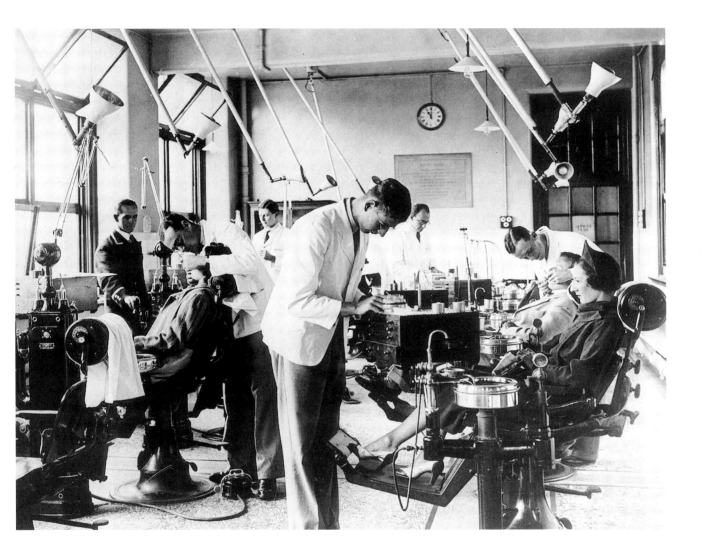

III 22. Conservative dentistry

The main clinic, the conservation room, is seen as it was in 1937. In the front row of chairs, on the left, each is equipped with a unit which carries an electrical drill, heated spray bottles and compressed air syringe. These units were fitted in 1935. The junior students, in the back row, have still to make do with foot engines. These unwieldy, slow but surprisingly precise devices, together with the heavy case of instruments – the student in the foreground is preparing a dressing on the top of his – had to be carried to the chairside for each working session. The predecessors of the lights on their swivelled telescopic arms were counter-poised on pulleys and were hauled down to working height with the aid of a hooked pole. It is interesting to note that each student in the picture is working without artificial light. Under the clock is the memorial tablet to Sir Francis Farmer. At this time the school had 43 students.

LONDON · HOSPITAL, WHITECHAPEL ROAD, E.1

TIME TABLE FOR PROBATIONERS ON DAY DUTY.

BREAKFAST 6.30 a.m.	WARDS 7 a.m.	OFF DUTY 3 hours daily before 6 p.m. Except on Sundays when it is 4 hrs * †	DINNER 12.45 to 1.15 p.m. OR 1.15 to 1.45 p.m.	WARDS 1.15 p.m. OR 1.45 p.m.	SUPPER 9.30 p.m.	IN BED 10.30 p.m.

TIME TABLE FOR PROBATIONERS ON NIGHT DUTY.

RISE 8.15 p.m.	SUPPER 8.50 p.m.	IN WARDS From 9.20 p.m. to 7.20 a.m.	DINNER 8.20 a.m.	OFF DUTY From 9 a.m. to 1 p.m.	IN BED 1.30 p.m.

* In addition, one half-hour off duty is allowed after the morning's work, as well as sufficient time for early lunch and tea at a convenient hour.
† Probationers must carefully observe the regulations printed in their Leave of Absence Book.
All Probationers attend the weekly Nursing Lecture at 8 p.m. on Wednesdays from the time they first enter the Training School.
Probationers preparing for the next Annual Examination attend, in addition to the weekly Lecture, one instruction class from 8 p.m. to 9 p.m., and two study classes every week, i.e., from 9 a.m. to 10 a.m. when on night duty, and from 1.45 p.m. to 2.45 p.m. when on day duty. This is in addition to, and not a part of, the regulation off duty time, except during the short period when a Probationer is on night duty.
Exceptions will be made to the General Time Table when on "Special duty" and on Sundays, when the "off duty" time is 4 hrs.
The off duty on Sundays is arranged so that all members of the Nursing Staff may attend Service once every Sunday, in addition to attendance at the Holy Communion Service if desired. The "London" is an unsectarian Hospital, attendance at Divine Service is not compulsory. Probationers are allowed one hour off duty on Sunday afternoons, in addition to the three hours "off duty" time.
Probationers on day duty will be entitled to a whole day's holiday every fortnight, from 7.30 p.m. the previous night (except in exceptional circumstances), until 10 p.m. the following day, without going into the wards at all. A late pass is granted occasionally on this day, and, if desired, breakfast in bed is allowed. Probationers on night duty are also entitled to a "day off" every fortnight spending the night away from the Hospital if desired and returning by 1 p.m. the following day.
For particulars concerning annual holidays and sick leave, see enclosed copy of Standing Orders for Probationers.

NURSES and PROBATIONERS are expected to make themselves familiar with the following regulations issued by order of the House-Committee, and to observe them faithfully—
Not to remain in their own wards or to visit in any other wards when off duty, except after obtaining a pass from the Matron's Office.
Not, at any time, to go to wards in which they are not working, except when sent on a special errand.
To adhere *quite punctually* to their respective Time-tables, and to be most particular in returning their wards at the *exact* time specified.
All talking in the thoroughfare wards, corridors, and stairs, is strictly forbidden; and Nurses and Probationers are requested to be quiet and orderly when crossing the garden.
Not to go into each others rooms or to remain talking in the corridors after 10 p.m. when on day duty, or after 1 p.m. when on night duty.
All lights to be extinguished in the bed-rooms by 10.30 p.m., except on Saturdays, when they may continue burning until 11 p.m. Electric light only is allowed; not lamps or candles.
To be neat and orderly in their bed-rooms, carefully observing the printed rules put up for their guidance in this respect, and leaving the rooms always fit for inspection. All money, jewellery and valuables are to be kept under lock and key, as no responsibility can be taken for anything missing, or articles of value may be brought to the Matron's Office for safe keeping.
Not to enter their wards out of uniform without permission from the Matron.
Not to absent themselves from meals without permission from the Matron.
They may not receive their friends, without obtaining an order from the Matron's Office.
All Probationers must have their letters addressed "Nurses Home," London Hospital; *and with the Christian as well as the Surname, to avoid mistakes.*
There are always several Nurses with the same surname on the large Nursing Staff of the London Hospital, Probationers are advised, for their own sakes, to impress on their correspondents the desirability of adding the Christian name to the address.

January, 1922.

Cass

a

III 23. Looking after the patients in hospital

Miss Dulcie Carr, a nurse of the twenties, reminisced: 'How well I remember going to breakfast at 6.20 a.m. and then dashing on duty at 6.55 a.m. (a) to get the best broom and hide it under a patient's bed! The brooms were so hairless that there was great competition to get the best. There was no water laid on in the wards, and the first job for the "Tredegar" was to wash and then fill the doctor's jug and basin, and fold the doctor's towel fanwise. Tea leaves were then thrown under the beds, and junior nurses swept and dusted the ward, whilst the "outside" nurse washed up the patients' breakfast things in a zinc bath which stood on a large wooden tray. Breakfasts and suppers were cooked by the nurses in the ward kitchen, on the one available gas ring. The ward had to be spick and span by 8.30 a.m., and the nurses, wearing their white sleeves (we wore coloured sleeves and stiff cuffs for meals) (b) collected, ready to kneel for prayers. Between our fingers we would watch Sister on her knees, looking under every bed, and the moment "Amen" was said she would ask who swept the ward that day. Either a little dust or a few tea-leaves had been left behind.'

LONDON HOSPITAL NURSES

b

b

a

III 24. Looking after patients in their homes

Miss Lückes formed the private nursing staff in 1886, realizing the great advantage to the image and to the finances of the hospital, as well as to the public, which would be derived from having nurses to attend private families (a). The private staff nurses met a wide variety of people able to afford their own nurse, including the British and European aristocracy, members of the middle classes and the newly rich industrialists from the East End. All these groups were wary of hospital treatment and preferred the comfort and privacy of their homes.

The 'private staff' in their green cloaks and bonnets (b) were for nearly sixty years The London's ambassadors.

NURSES HOME STAFF LONDON HOSPITAL 2·12·15

a

III 25. Housemaids

The housemaids, ranging from teenagers to middle-aged women (*a*), were resident and most doubled as waitresses. The routine was a harsh one; they were on duty at 6.30 a.m. to serve nurses' breakfasts, and finished at 9.30 p.m. with the serving of nurses' suppers. They had one day off each month and this started only at 9.00 a.m.

Senior sisters, some of whom had a canary or a parrot (*b*), received a high standard of service, including a morning call. A raw new maid, instructed by her senior, was told: 'You say Good Morning Sister, pull back the curtains and uncover the old bird.' Being used to younger brothers, she did just that.

b

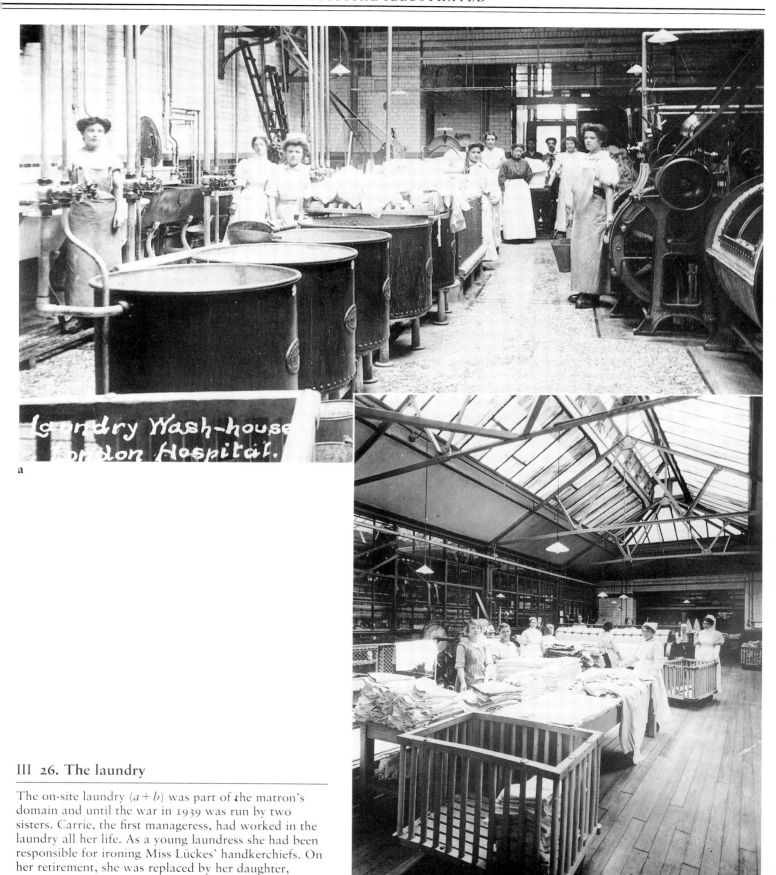

III 26. The laundry

The on-site laundry (*a* + *b*) was part of the matron's domain and until the war in 1939 was run by two sisters. Carrie, the first manageress, had worked in the laundry all her life. As a young laundress she had been responsible for ironing Miss Lückes' handkerchiefs. On her retirement, she was replaced by her daughter, 'young Carrie'.

LONDON HOSPITAL INDOOR UNIFORM.

a

LONDON HOSPITAL INDOOR UNIFORM.

b

SISTERS' NEW UNIFORM

NURSES' NEW UNIFORM

d

e

III 27. The uniform

Until 1927, long hair was mandatory – it was parted in the middle and put up in a bun (*a*). Check sleeves were worn to meals and off duty. On duty one took off the check sleeves and replaced them with white ones (*b*). To speak to a doctor bare-armed was just not done nor to sweep without gloves on.

Wartime rationing of all materials made changes to the uniform essential. The leg-of-mutton sleeves disappeared on the advice of Norman Hartnell and were replaced in 1941 by puff sleeves (*c* + *d*). A uniform department in the charge of an experienced dressmaker was opened and aprons were worn only when on duty in the wards. This measure saved 2,760 yards of dress material and 1,680 aprons each year, besides reducing laundering. Brown shoes and stockings replaced the unpopular black ones.

Further changes took place in 1986; these also came from the Hartnell salon (*e*).

a

b

III 28. The London Hospital Badge and League of Nurses

Miss Monk (*a*) took over from Eva Lückes in 1919 and was matron until 1931 when she was succeeded by Miss Littleboy. Miss Monk was subsequently president of the Royal College of Nursing from 1938 to 1940. The London Hospital League of Nurses was founded by her in 1931 to form a bond between present and former members of the nursing staff who trained at The London Hospital School of Nursing. The badge (*b*), made of silver, was available in two sizes for members to purchase if they wished. In 1943 when the training course was revised, the board of governors, and later the special trustees, provided for these badges to be presented to all nurses completing training and passing the Final State Examination.

III 29. Sir William Goschen – new chairman

Viscount Knutsford died in The London on 27 July 1931 aged 76. Sir William Goschen succeeded him as chairman at a difficult time. England was forced off the gold standard, the slump continued, unemployment was widespread. Little money was forthcoming. Nevertheless his quiet friendliness won through and during his chairmanship a new cardiac department and new isolation wards were opened. There was a fine new department of physical medicine, private wards, gynaecology department and the Brentwood Annexe with 360 beds.

a

b

III 30. Patients

Patience was a virtue that both visitors and patients learnt quickly. Patiently they waited to visit relatives (*a*) or to be seen by the doctor (*b*). It was not done to complain nor to seek participation in one's care; patients' rights were as yet unsought.

XMAS, 1935

We are the stars that come out in the night
To make the London Hospital bright.
On our knees we polish and rub,
Brasses we brighten and floors we scrub.
When Christmas arrives we feel hale and hearty,
Down go our tools and we join in a party.

a

b

III 31. The 'night scrubbers' party

The night scrubbers were the fifty or so women who, from 11 p.m. to 5 a.m., cleaned all departments, offices and corridors. One unique feature of their Christmas party (a + b) was that, though no food was left over, nothing was eaten. Each guest had a bag on her lap and every sandwich, sausage roll and bun went home. Many scrubbers stayed for years, but every evening a handful of women came hoping that there might be an absentee or two and they might get six hours work for three shillings and eleven pence.

a

b

III 32. Christmas 'Angels and Fairies'

For many weeks before Christmas the nursing staff practised carols. When the day came, the long procession waited in a darkened corridor; the conductor's baton tapped; the violins gave the note; and Christmas was ushered in with 'Christians Awake'. A carol was sung in each ward as the procession wound slowly round. Babies in the children's ward slept through 'Sleep Holy Babe', adults sat up, joined in, or wept. It was the best part of Christmas. Then for the fun, the wards were decorated and everyone wore a motto (a).

Each year Father Christmas attended by his fairies tours the wards. The fairies (b), usually the toughest of rugger players, are transformed for the morning, once by the linen room but nowadays by the theatre staff who make their tutus and wings. Given Dutch courage by a champagne breakfast, they start their marathon tour giving each patient a Christmas present, and each nurse a bunch of Devon violets, the latter in exchange for a kiss.

III 33. Medical students

In the 1930s a group of 70–75 male students entered the Medical College each year. Women had been accepted between 1918 and 1922 and again during the Second World War. The students played an active part in the medical care given by the hospital acquiring practical skills in the wards and in the out-patients department. They learned at first hand of the poverty in the East End. They also played hard, often excelling at sports,

particularly rugby, and enjoyed their social life. Socializing with nurses was officially discouraged and thus became a tempting pastime. On Christmas Day students assisted with giving lunch to the patients and then, in small bands or 'troupes', toured the wards entertaining the patients. After the war the 'troupes' were abandoned and a Christmas show took their place and continues today.

a

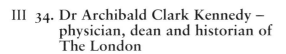

b

c

III 34. Dr Archibald Clark Kennedy – physician, dean and historian of The London

Dr Archie Clark-Kennedy (a), 'C-K', (1893–1985) died shortly before the celebration of the bicentenary of the medical college – to which he had given unstinting service as dean for seventeen years. This period covered the Second World War and the difficult years which followed. He had an abiding interest in medical education, emphasizing in his teaching and writing both the science and the humanity of medicine, and constantly exhorting the recognition of the patient as a person. He is remembered as a man of remarkable physical, intellectual and moral stature (b + c). He wrote many books including a two-volume history entitled *The London, a Study in the Voluntary Hospital System* (1963), and a shorter version *London Pride* (1973). These are models of scholarship and good writing and are fitting memorials to his life of devotion to the hospital.

III 35. Coat of Arms

The coat of arms combines the cross of The London,
the three feathers (representing the tavern where the
hospital was founded), and the motto 'I am human
therefore any human concern is my concern'.

III 36. Dr Donald Hunter – physician, teacher and pioneer in occupational medicine

Dr Donald Hunter (1889–1978) was a memorable teacher of clinical medicine to generations of students at The London. His style was individual and enthusiastic and he was endowed with 'fire in the belly' (a term he often used). Outside The London, he was best known as the country's leading authority on occupational medicine. His book *The Diseases of Occupations* (1955) became a classic as soon as it was published. The enormous experience upon which the book was based was largely derived from his knowledge of East Enders, many of whom worked in the countless industries which then existed locally.

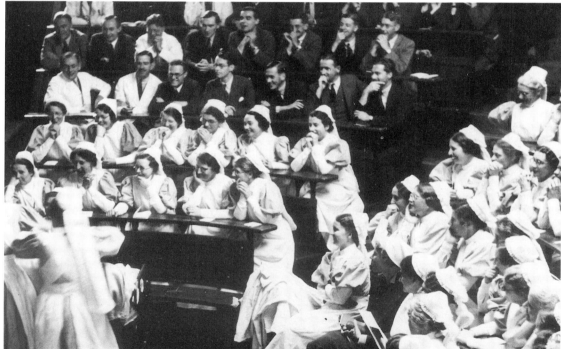

III 37. Evacuation, 1939

At the outbreak of the Second World War, The London Hospital became a casualty hospital and parent hospital to two sectors of London and the home counties, comprising north and east London, the whole of Essex and part of Hertfordshire and Middlesex. Staff and equipment were transferred from The London to hospitals in these areas (*a*). These included 86 doctors, 427 students, 408 nurses, 61 radiographers, theatre attendants, dispensers and laboratory assistants, and 25 clerical staff.

The briefing prior to this challenging exercise is portrayed above (*b*). The doctors and nurses, with an air of excitement, are awaiting the unknown.

III 38. Ready for action

The midwives were ready to sally forth in their tin hats (*a*) to deliver the babies who arrived often in the middle of an air raid. The Luckes Home basement rooms were converted into nursing staff sleeping accommodation (*b*) and tea-making equipment, hurricane lamps and candlesticks were ready for use in emergency.

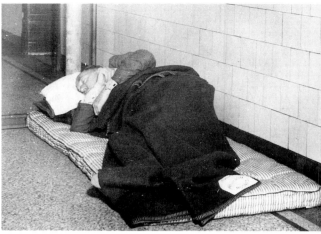

III 39. Management in action

Two of the staff who played important roles are portrayed here. Captain Brierley (*a*) was an ex-regular soldier and adjutant who was appointed steward and then in 1939 house governor. He was appointed lay officer to both wartime sectors, organizing the distribution of equipment and lay staff, but himself staying behind in The London with a small band of staff. Henry Brierley was a tower of strength, being general administrator, fire-fighter and friend to all. He is seen above (*b*) exhausted but tin hat at the ready.

George Neligan (*c*) was one of the surgeons who stayed behind to 'hold the fort'. He was an outstanding personality displaying a tremendous air of calm whilst accomplishing so much. He is seen above (*d*) snatching a brief period of sleep in the corridor between fire-fighting and operating.

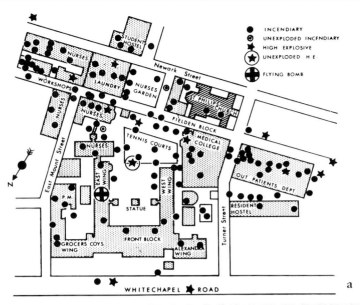

III 40. Bombing of London

This map (a) of bombs on The London speaks for itself – it was a miracle that it was possible to organize care for patients under such adversity. The years 1940 and 1941 were a time of great suffering for the people of London and saw much damage to The London itself. The docks and surrounding area had always played a large part in the life of the hospital and during the war the two were drawn even closer together. The illustrations above show the damage inflicted by bombs both on the hospital and on the docks (b)*.

*Reproduced by kind permission of the Museum of London (Port of London Authority Archives).

III 41. Disaster

Miss Margaret Broadley, who was tutor at the time, reminisces: 'The night that a bomb went through the cookery classroom and exploded in the laundry, the adjacent nurses' home suffered damage. The previous evening, another tutor Miss Annie Harris and myself had, with some difficulty, prepared the cookery classroom for a practical nursing examination. As we left, we surveyed our handiwork. "This classroom is hopeless," I said. "What it needs is a bomb on it!" We next met at 5 a.m. My colleague who had already inspected the damage exclaimed, "You've had your wish!"'

III 42. Hope

The hospital garden has been the scene of many events – the erection of Queen Alexandra's statue, Sir William Paulin's gift of the covered way, the bombing of the east wing, royal visits. Nothing, however, catches the spirit of The London more than these midwives digging for victory in such unlikely soil. 'Not failure but low aim is crime' was one of Miss Lückes' maxims and, whether or not the potatoes did well, The London's spirit clearly manifested itself.

III 43. 200th Anniversary of the hospital – 1940

The visit of the King and Queen in 1940 at a time when the hospital was trying to celebrate its bicentenary was a great boost to morale. The hospital had already received several direct hits, and many hospital workers from the surrounding estate had also lost their homes. Their Majesties are seen here talking to staff who had suffered such losses.

III 44. Wartime Annexe at Brentwood

The London Hospital Annexe at Brentwood (*a*) was opened in 1941. Note the old-fashioned stove (*b*); these were widely used in the emergency hospitals. The patients are smoking, something universally acceptable at that time. Even the nurse was encouraging smoking by offering one of the soldiers a light.

III 45. A new chairman

Sir John Mann, chairman of Mann, Crossman and
Paulin Ltd, became chairman of The London in 1943,
succeeding Sir William Goschen. He had already served
on the house committee for a quarter of a century and
been treasurer for nineteen years. In 1951, he married
the matron Miss Clare Alexander which caused much
excitement among staff at the time!

III 46. Clare Alexander

Clare Alexander, appointed matron in 1941, had been
the first qualified sister tutor of The London from 1935
to 1938 when she left to become matron of
Addenbrookes Hospital. She was an efficient
administrator, committed to improving both patient
care and nurse training. During the war she and Annie
Harris, senior sister tutor, maintained continuity of
training for student nurses widely dispersed in sector
hospitals. They introduced the study-day system of
training in 1945 and the training period was reduced to
three years.

At The London Miss Alexander made many changes.
Nurses' duty hours were reduced to 96 a fortnight, and
a system of three months' long-service leave and
improved pensions for those retiring were introduced.
The patient's day was reappraised with a later
breakfast time of 8.00 a.m. and the time nurses spent on
domestic tasks was reduced with the appointment of
ward orderlies. She assumed control of the operating
theatres and nurses were able to gain operating-room
experience. She obtained agreement that up to 10 per
cent of the nurses appointed annually should have been
trained elsewhere and, as a result, a number of nurses
from Australia and New Zealand joined The London.

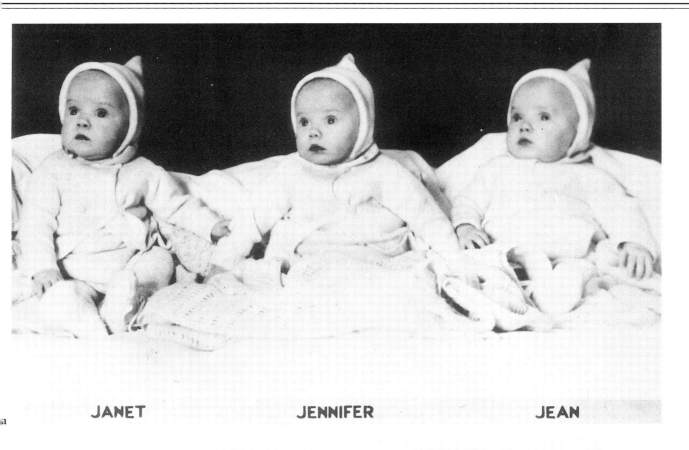

JANET   JENNIFER   JEAN

THE WILSON TRIPLETS

BORN AT THE LONDON HOSPITAL
ON
16TH JULY 1943

FINGER PRINTS DISSIMILAR

RIGHT RING FINGER
IMPRESSION OF
JANET

RIGHT RING FINGER
IMPRESSION OF
JENNIFER

RIGHT RING FINGER
IMPRESSION OF
JEAN

III 47. An interesting case

Jennifer, Janet and Jean were identical triplets (*a*) born at The London in 1943. So alike were they that the doctors suggested their fingerprints might be identical. Scotland Yard were called to the scene – the result was a great relief for the Yard (*b*). Dactyloscopy was confirmed as an exact scientific method for distinguishing individual human beings – even triplets!

III 48. A baby boom

Most of the midwifery unit was evacuated to Hertfordshire during the war but on its return to The London in 1946 faced an increase in the birth rate. The department was often short of beds but it was an extremely happy team. Obstetric students and pupil midwives worked together in Mary Northcliffe and Marie Celeste wards. The medical students then gained experience on the District under the guidance of Sister Miss Gladys Haynes, 'Auntie Glad'. The pupil midwives went on to Queen Mary's Maternity Hospital at Hampstead. Here Sister Miss Elizabeth Major holds a handful of triplets, John, Helen and Catherine Easton, born in the 1960s.

IV · The London in the NHS: 1948–1990

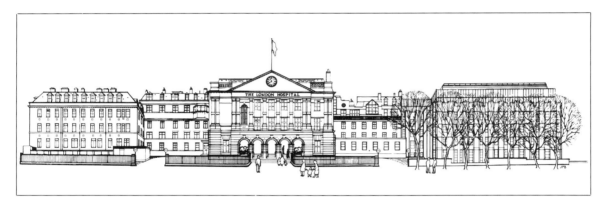

IV 1. The National Health Service dawns

Bertrand Dawson was a powerful advocate of a national approach to health care, a concept which had received increasing support during the war years. His influence was particularly crucial during discussions arising from the White Paper which preceded the National Health Service Act of 1946. He died in 1945, before the Act was passed, and three years before the NHS became a reality.

The last meeting of the Court of Governors under the voluntary system. From left to right: Col.Cahusac (Assistant Secretary), Col. Marlborough Pryor, D.S.O. in the Chair (Sir John Mann was ill at the time), Capt. Brierley. Behind the Chairman hangs the portrait of Sir Ernest Morris, House Governor under Lord Knutsford. In the corner, the bust of the Founder, John Harrison, looks on.

IV 2. The last day

Apprehension concerning the changes represented by the introduction of the NHS was unfounded. At The London the transition from voluntary hospital to NHS hospital was effected with ease largely due to the fact that the same people retained the senior posts. Sir John Mann remained chairman, Clare Alexander remained matron and Captain Brierley became secretary to the board of governors. In addition, Dr Clark-Kennedy continued as dean of the medical college. When formulating local policies common sense and pragmatism prevailed; for instance, it was decided that the private wards and consulting rooms in Fielden House should continue provided the income they generated covered their costs. However the scheme for private nurses to work outside the hospital was dropped.

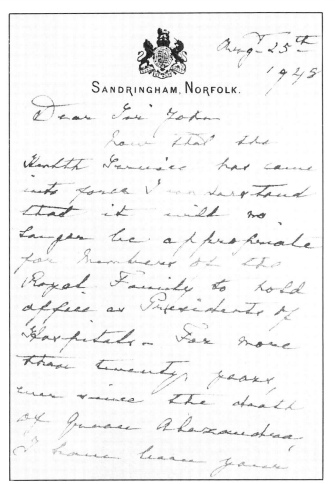

IV 3. From president to patron

Throughout the London's history, until the advent of the NHS, the hospital had been honoured by royal presidents as titular heads of the institution. Each had been held in high esteem, and The London had benefited greatly from their influence. Queen Mary was the last of many royal presidents, an office which the constitution of the NHS no longer recognized. Instead, Queen Mary consented to become patron of The London jointly with her son, King George VI.

IV 4. Queen Elizabeth II becomes patron

Upon the death of George VI, Queen Elizabeth II became patron of the hospital. She is shown here on her visit in 1954.

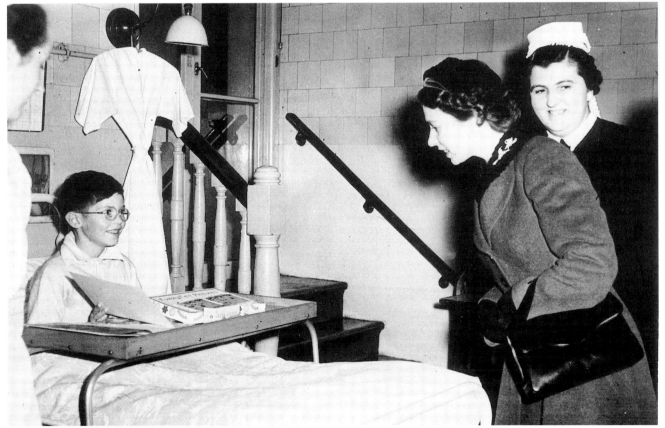

a

b

IV 5. Radio doctor

Dr Charles Hill (*a*) (1904–1989), who became Lord Hill of Luton, qualified from The London in 1929. In the dark days of the war he was the BBC's first radio doctor, becoming a very popular broadcaster. He talked of everyday medical concerns in a convincing, matter-of-fact and reassuring way, and his deep booming voice was immediately recognizable. As secretary of the British Medical Association he had a key role in guiding the medical profession into the NHS. Subsequently he had a distinguished career in politics, and later, in the highest offices in broadcasting. Dr Richard Bomford (1907–1981), physician to The London (*b*), succeeded Charles Hill as radio doctor, broadcasting good sense and wisdom to an eager public. Dick Bomford is remembered for his devoted service to The London throughout his career.

LONDON HOSPITAL PRAYER.

SILENCE PLEASE.   **(Men's Wards.)**

LET US PRAY.

    ALMIGHTY and Everloving God, Who didst send Thine only Son Jesus Christ to be the Saviour of men, we pray Thee as earnestly as we can to bless the work done at the London Hospital. Bless all those, whether rich or poor, who have denied themselves to help the Hospital.

    Help all those who are nurses to have always present to their minds the example of our Blessed Saviour's love and sympathy for the poor and suffering. Give them grace and patience faithfully to fulfil their holy calling, doing all as unto Thee, and we pray Thee to crown their work with success and happiness. We commend O God, the patients to Thy loving care. Soothe their pain; relieve their anxiety; lead them to a knowledge and love of Thee; give them patience under their sufferings, and a happy ending to all their trouble. We pray Thee also to remember the wives and children of the men here, and to help them in their trouble and distress. Grant this, we humbly beseech Thee, O God, for Thy Son Jesus Christ's sake. Amen.   **357**

a

b

IV 6. Spirit of service

At the annual general meeting of the League of Nurses in June 1948, Clare Alexander said: 'The spirit of the hospital will be there in the new health service. . . . I am sure, when we meet again . . . the hospital will still be The London.' The tradition of dedication and service as expressed here in the hospital prayer (*a*), so vital in the work and life of the hospital, did indeed survive and continue. On a practical level, however, there were some welcome innovations such as the installation of gas fires in the wards (*b*). Porters no longer had to carry coke and coal up stairs and along corridors in order to keep ward fires stoked up.

a

b

IV 7. The London Hospital and its annexes

In July 1948, the bed complement of The London Hospital including its annexes was 1091. The annexes, which were administered directly from The London, had been acquired at different times to meet different needs and were dispersed over south-east England from Queen Mary's Maternity Home in Hampstead to the Herman De Stern Convalescent Home in Felixstowe. Shown here are Banstead (*a*), Brentwood (*b*) and Fairfield in Reigate (*c*). After transfer to the NHS services came to be concentrated increasingly on the Whitechapel site and the importance of the annexes diminished. This, together with administrative difficulties, led gradually to the closure of the annexes. Patients, meanwhile, continued to be referred to The London from far and wide, and particularly from counties to the north and east of London.

IV 8. Sir John Mann's retirement

Upon his retirement Sir John Mann was presented with his portrait painted by James Gunn, a gift to him from the nursing staff. He was succeeded by Sir Harry Moore, who was a director of Hill Samuel, merchant bankers. Earlier, as chairman of the building committee, Sir Harry had reported that a comprehensive plan for rebuilding the hospital at Whitechapel had been agreed in principle. The expansion of the hospital at Whitechapel to accommodate 800 beds, and the closure of Brentwood Annexe, were achieved during his term of office.

SCANNING FACE OF A FINER LONDON YET TO BE

A **STUDENT NURSE,** sees " The Shape of Things to Come " in a model of a New East End—a vision which will become fact when labour and materials make it possible for the new London Hospital (as shown within the dotted lines) to emerge from the plans made for its reconstruction. This great modern medical centre, created by the Hospital's architects, will arise within the framework of the Master Plan which the Architect to the London County Council has proposed for East London. The model was made by members of the L.C.C. staff at County Hall.

COMPLETE RECONSTRUCTION TO MARK THIRD CENTURY OF SERVICE

IV 9. Great plans

After the war not only were damaged wards and departments in need of repair but new facilities were required to meet the needs of medical advances. Plans for redevelopment conceived as the war ended were too grandiose: shortages of skilled labour, of building materials and of funds had not been anticipated and plans had to be scaled down in the light of these shortages. In common with other former voluntary hospitals, however, The London did retain some degree of financial autonomy, enabling 'free funds' (i.e. legacies and donations) to be used to help in the reconstruction.

a

b

c

IV 10. Ancient trees make way for modern buildings

The need for new buildings such as the Institute of Pathology (*a*) and the Dental School (*b*) (funded jointly by the Ministry of Health and the University Grants Committee), and the new ward block, was undeniable. The environmental effect, however, was considerable.

Many Londoners were saddened by the loss of the 'Garden of Eden' and a large part of the hospital garden that resulted from the erection of these buildings (*c*).

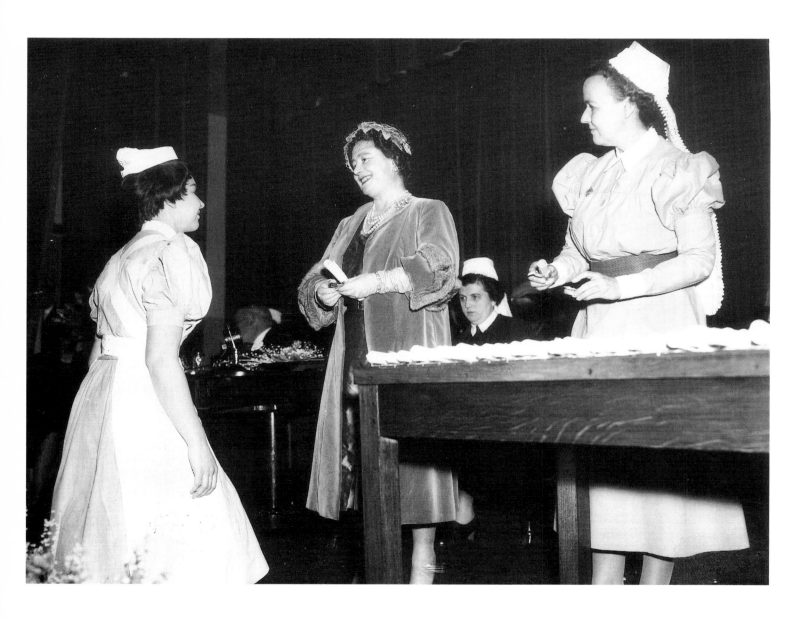

IV 11. Miss Ceris Jones

Miss Ceris Jones, matron from 1957 to 1961, continued Clare Alexander's focus on nurse education, but widened its scope. She established a programme of study days for sisters and also persuaded the board of governors that new teaching accommodation was essential if recruitment was to be maintained. She is seen here seated behind the Queen Mother at the presentation of badges and certificates.

IV 12. The Princess Alexandra School of Nursing

Throughout its history The London has benefited from the generosity of individuals whose legacies and donations have helped to erect many of the hospital buildings. The School of Nursing is no exception to this; building was made possible by a combination of government funds and covenants from benefactors. Sir Giles Guthrie and his sister covenanted £50,000 towards the building of the school and Sir Giles is seen here at the opening ceremony speaking with Princess Alexandra after whom the school is named. Also in the photograph are matron Miss (later Dame) Phyllis Friend, principal tutor Miss Sheila Collins, and house governor Mr John Scarlett.

a

b

IV 13. The tradition of medical teaching at The London

William Blizard started a new approach to medical education when he founded the London Hospital Medical College in 1785. In appealing for funds to establish the college he argued the need for teaching both the principles and the practice of physic and surgery. He was later assisted by Archibald Billing, who was the first in London to introduce organized clinical teaching. Teachers were practising clinicians who taught as much by example as by precept. The London continues to have a reputation for pioneering new approaches; in addition, there have been frequent adaptations, both in educational content and method, to meet the changing needs of medical students. Since the war, the role of academic departments has become increasingly important. In particular the work of Professor Clifford Wilson should be mentioned. The London has been fortunate to have had many clinicians on its staff who have also been inspiring and memorable teachers. The illustrations show a teaching ward round conducted by Lord Brain (*a*) and a lecture demonstration by Dr William Evans (*b*).

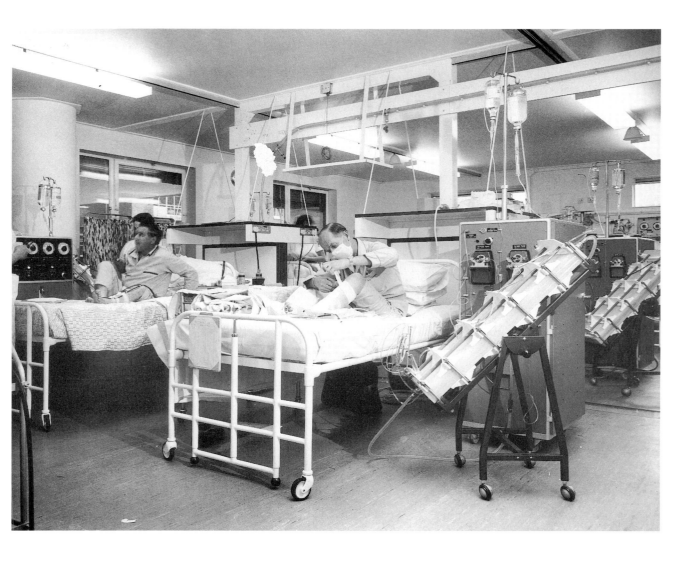

IV 14. Advances in treatment for diseases of the kidney

For half a century The London has been in the forefront of research and treatment of diseases of the kidney; for example, an important classification of various types of nephritis was based on The London Hospital system. In 1959 the hospital received its first artificial kidney, a donation from a patient who was himself a doctor with renal failure, and renal transplants have been performed at The London since 1968. Swapping of kidneys between centres to ensure optimal matching was pioneered at The London, and the St John's Ambulance Airwing was established to transport kidneys as rapidly as possible. Seen here in the photograph is Hanbury ward, developed as a dialysis day centre in 1971. The hospital now provides the largest centre for dialysis and transplantation in London.

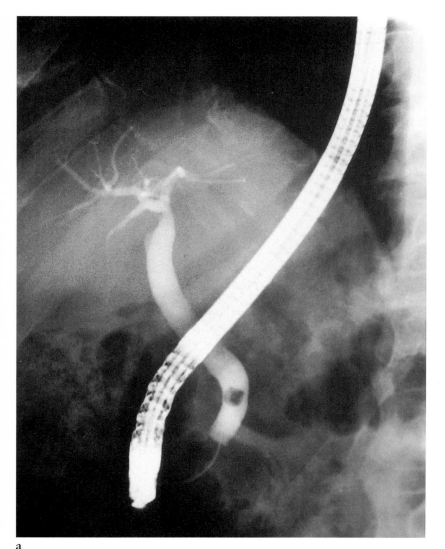

a

b

IV 15. Painless surgery

Although many operations still need incisions to give wide access to diseased organs, in certain areas cutting surgery is now replaced by the use of tiny telescopes, often made of flexible glass fibres through which the surgeon can see and deal with stones, cancers and other diseases in the kidney, bladder, gall bladder, stomach, colon, knee joint and many other parts. Twenty-five years ago The London pioneered these methods in the surgery of the prostate and bladder. Today it continues to lead in the use of painless flexible endoscopes in the treatment of disorders of many other organs. Here a gastroduodenoscope has been slipped into the duodenum (*a*), allowing dye to be injected into the common bile duct to outline a stone. Later, through the same endoscope, the stone will be removed, and the patient saved from a major operation. A fine quartz fibre is used to shine laser light through the endoscope (*b*) – it is used to destroy little cancers in some organs, and stop bleeding from ulcers in others.

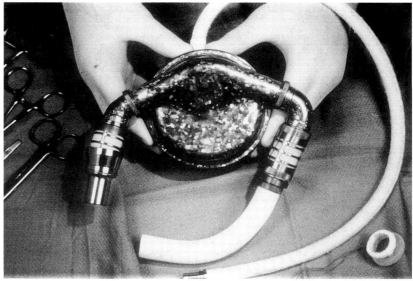

a

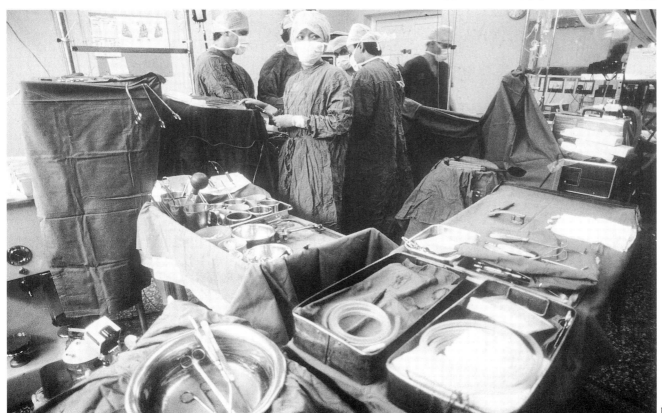

b

IV 16. Advances in treatment for the heart and lungs

Post-war technological advances and greatly improved anaesthetic methods have made major heart and lung surgery almost routine. The community benefits, as patients who would previously have been invalids return to work; and the quality of life for such patients is greatly improved. The use of an artificial heart device (the 'tin heart') (a), a bridge to heart transplantation, is the latest achievement of a surgeon at The London keeping the hospital in the forefront of this speciality.

Drs William Evans and Wallace Brigden helped to establish The London as a leading centre for the treatment of cardiac disease. The work continues apace today (b) with a major role being given to dissolving clots occluding arteries after heart attacks, and the use of 'balloons' and lasers for dilating narrowed vessels. Equally important is the hospital's role in the prevention of cardiac disease and in health education.

b

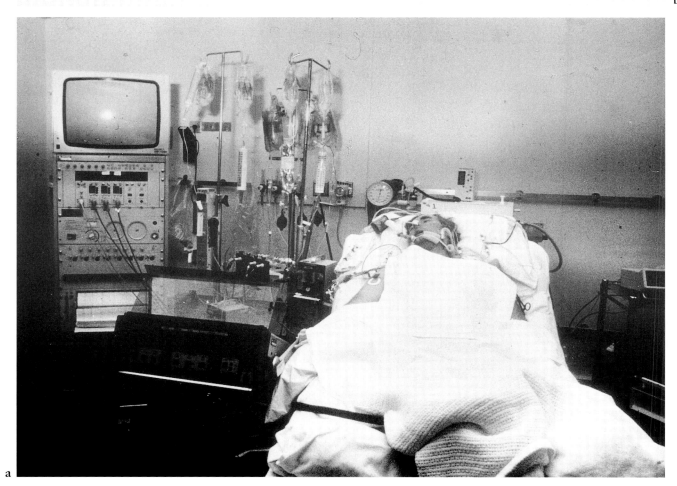

a

IV 17. Treatment of the seriously ill

Patients who are critically ill, or who have undergone major surgery or trauma and may require artificial ventilation, need highly specialized medical and nursing care. Such patients are cared for in an intensive therapy unit. Computer-aided equipment monitors the patient's progress and assists in treatment. The 'battery' of equipment is seen here (*a*) as is also the method of transport for some patients in the future (*b*) whose survival may depend on speed of reaching such treatment.

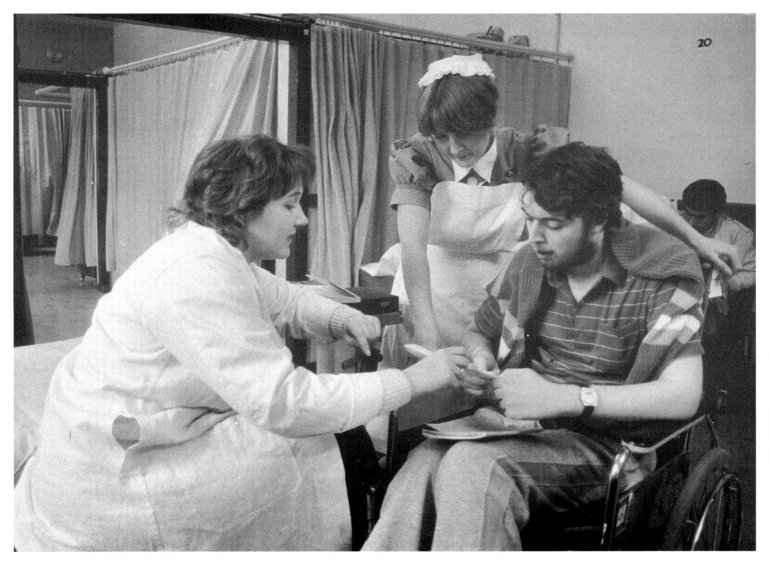

IV 18. Neurology and neurosurgery – advances in treatment

Continuing the work of the hospital's earlier pioneers in neurology and neurosurgery, The London today maintains its lead in research and treatment of diseases of the brain and the nerves. Russell Brain was a leading neurologist, peer, and President of the Royal College of Physicians: his successors today have expanded his work into unimaginable new fields. The relief of incurable pain by the use of neurostimulators; the diagnosis of disorders by measuring the speed with which nerve impulses pass down a single nerve fibre; and surgery on the brain through tiny needles instead of enormous incisions – all these are being pioneered at The London.

Rehabilitation following neurosurgery is important. Here a speech therapist and a ward sister help a patient in the neurosurgical ward who had lost his speech due to a head injury.

Observation

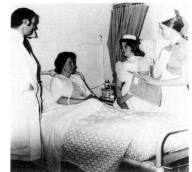

Doctor's ward round

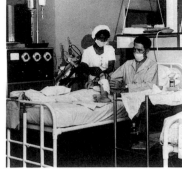

Training in Renal Dialysis

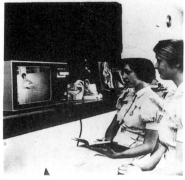

Education

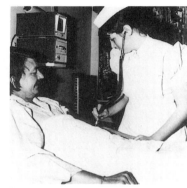

Checking blood pressure

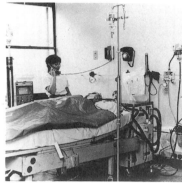

Intensive care

A place to study and relax

Special baby care

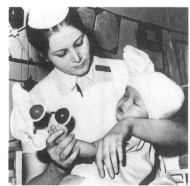

Caring for a child

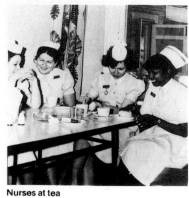

Nurses at tea

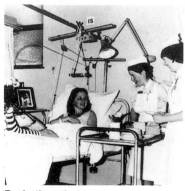

Tea for the patients

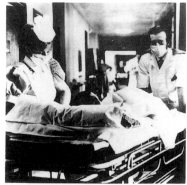

Nurses receiving a patient

IV 19. Daily patient care

In conjunction with major medical advances, the
observation and care of a patient goes on day and night.

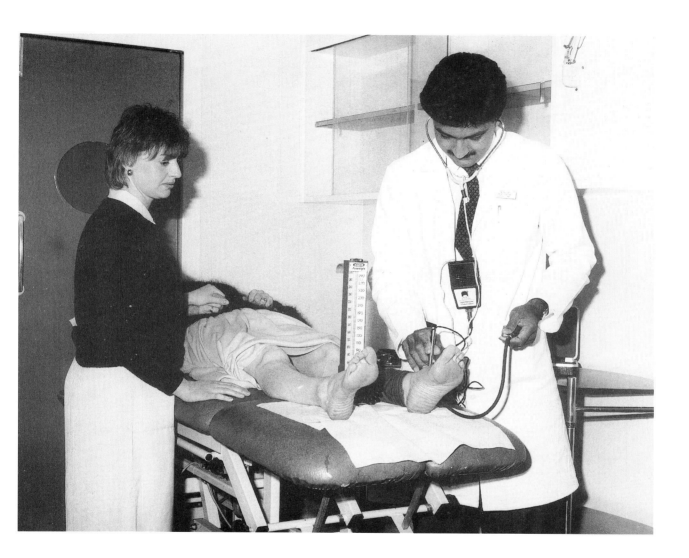

IV 20. From Top to Toe

The paramedical services are a crucial support to medical care. Audiologists, chiropodists, dieticians, occupational therapists, orthoptists, physiotherapists, psychologists, radiographers and speech therapists work with doctors to ensure the full recovery of body and mind. Their scientific training, skill and dedication are of great importance to patients in the hospital, clinics and health centres served by the health authority.

The London has a full range of paramedical services many of which have achieved international recognition for their work in improving the quality of patient care. Departmental heads are often requested to take part in radio and television programmes and to speak at international conferences. Shown here is the work of chiropodists helping to correct physical defects which greatly impair the enjoyment of a normal life.

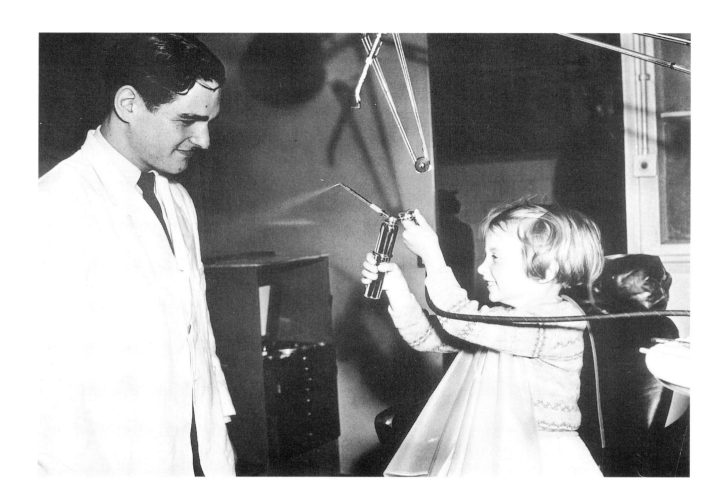

IV 21. A visit to the dentist

An important part of the dentist's work is putting the
patient at ease. This is particularly important with
children. Here a dental student is making a very good
start in establishing a rapport.

IV 22. The Dental Polyclinic

Some twenty years ago the main clinic in the dental institute became known as the polyclinic because a co-ordinated approach to the practice and teaching of all phases of preventive and restorative dentistry took place there. At the time this photograph was taken (1968) treatment of patients in a supine posture was an innovation.

a

b

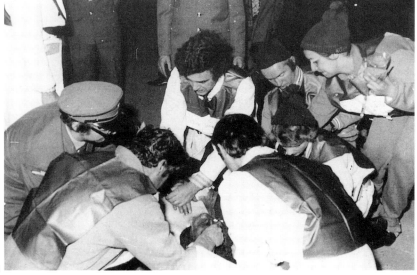

c

IV 23. Orthopaedics and trauma

The word 'orthopaedics' was first used during the Enlightenment at about the time The London was founded, and when a more humanitarian concern was shown towards crippled children. The term came to embrace surgical treatment of all bones and joints, the surgical speciality becoming very closely linked with the much more recent discipline of medical rheumatology.

Since the war, both specialties at The London have maintained a leading national position. Dr Michael Mason (1917–1977), rheumatologist at The London, had a powerful influence both on the emergence of rheumatology from its origins in physical medicine, and on emphasizing the interdependence of the two specialties. Research in recent years at The London has been particularly productive in the development of new forms of artificial joints, resulting in great benefit to many patients suffering from immobility and joint pains. The illustrations show a case conference taking place (*a*), and the emergency team from The London helping at the Moorgate underground train disaster in 1975 (*b* + *c*).

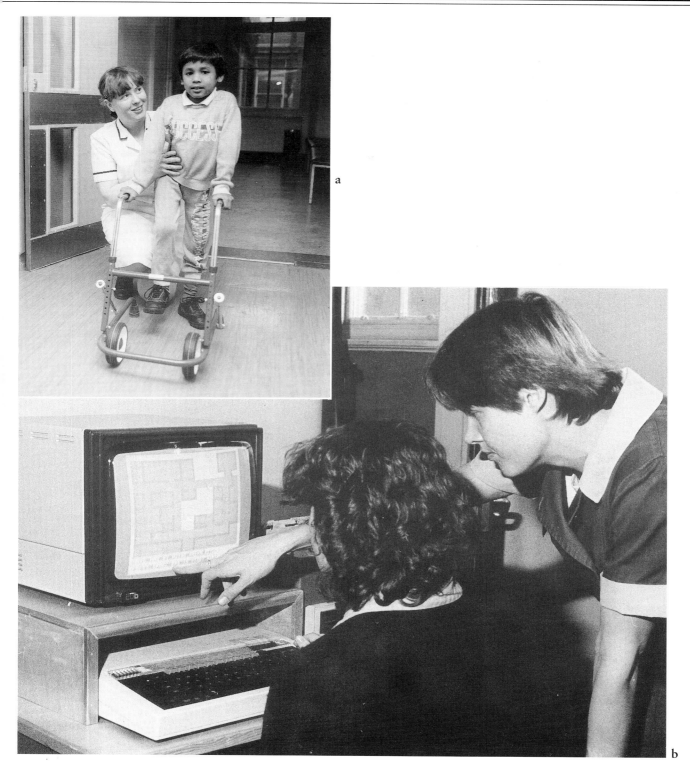

a

b

IV 24. The road to recovery

There is often a long gap between finishing treatment and returning to work; expert help from the physiotherapist can help to close it. At the command of King George V The London Hospital started its school of physiotherapy, the first in the country: today it flourishes. Here a physiotherapist is teaching an eight-year-old to walk again after a serious leg injury that needed several operations (*a*). The occupational therapist may also be called in to help a disabled patient to return to normal life (*b*). The London runs the first university course in occupational therapy.

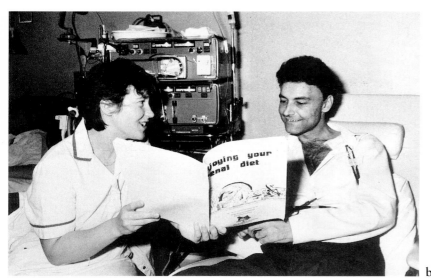

b

a

IV 25. Feeding the hospital – catering, nutrition and dietetics

Many thousands of people are treated in and work at the hospital each year. All have to be fed, but their requirements or desires differ greatly. Provision of the right food at the right time is the job of the catering staff (a). At The London each year several million meals are produced.

The role of the dietitian (b) in the provision of hospital food is also of crucial importance; many patients need advice on both the content and the quantity of their food. Dietitians also play an important role in promoting health in the community, particularly amongst children, the elderly and ethnic groups. In the photograph the dietitian discusses with a renal patient the kind of diet that should be followed for this type of disorder once the patient has returned home.

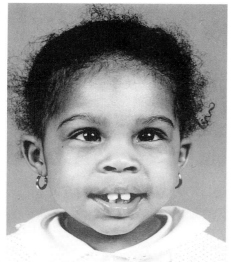

a

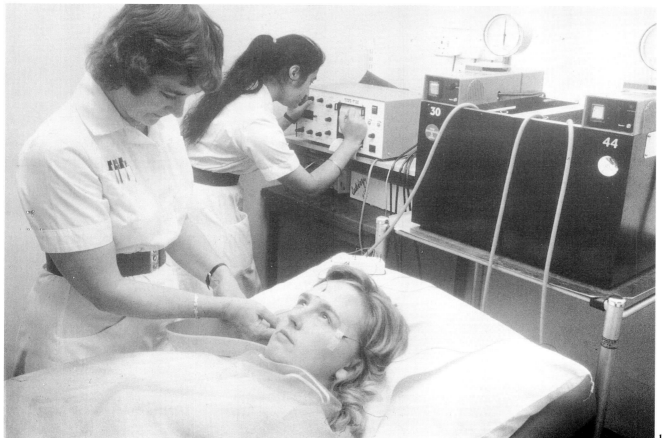

b

IV 26. Sight and hearing restored

The use of lasers and microsurgery has produced dramatic improvements in the treatment of eye disease. At the same time, much longer-term and repetitious work goes on. Seen here is a child who first attended with a severe squint. At 17 months following treatment by the orthoptist, the defect has been corrected (a).

ENT surgeons' work is vital to another of our senses – that of hearing. Some tumours are removed by the collaborative effort of an ear and brain surgeon; the aim is always to help the patient escape the lonely world of silence. Seen here is the audiologist (b) carrying out a vestibular test on a young patient.

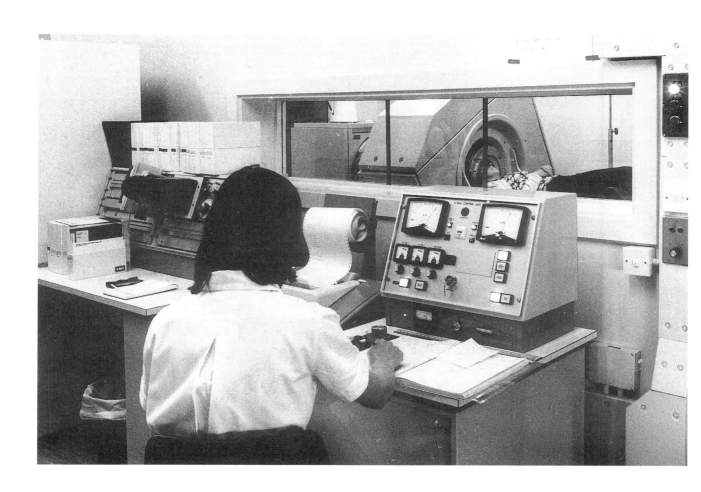

IV 27. Cancer treatment

There have been enormous advances in the treatment of cancer since Sir Henry Souttar went to Paris to meet Mme Curie and discuss the way radium might be used. Later Souttar persuaded the Medical Research Council to give The London the first precious gramme of radium which he used to treat breast cancer. Today the hospital continues in the lead with megavoltage treatment of cancer of many organs. There are some cancers that still have to be cut out by surgery; others respond entirely to radiation; yet others melt away with chemotherapy. A generous benefaction from The Grand Metropolitan Company endowed the Maxwell Joseph Readership in Oncology and as a result The London continues to be in the lead in the treatment of cancer. Here the radiographer is using a CT scanner to map the exact site of the cancer so that the megavoltage ray will be directed only at the growth, and spare the surrounding healthy tissue.

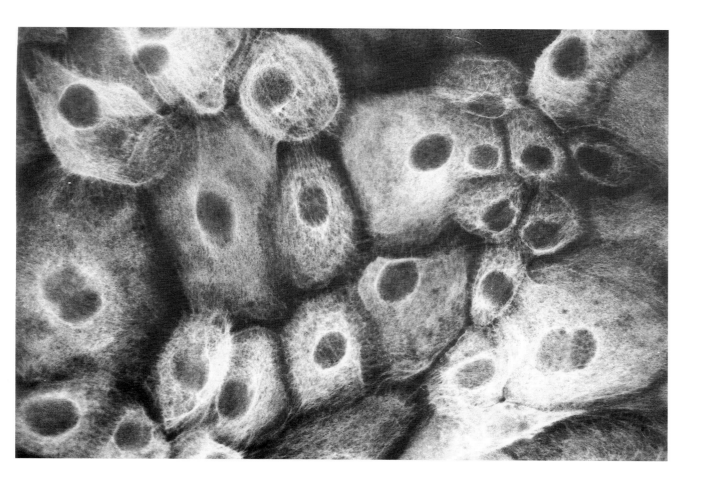

IV 28. New skin for old

One among several exciting and useful subjects of research in the Skin Department at The London involves growing skin cells in the laboratory to produce cultures of tissue; these can then be used as new skin to promote healing of chronic ulcers and to cover burns.

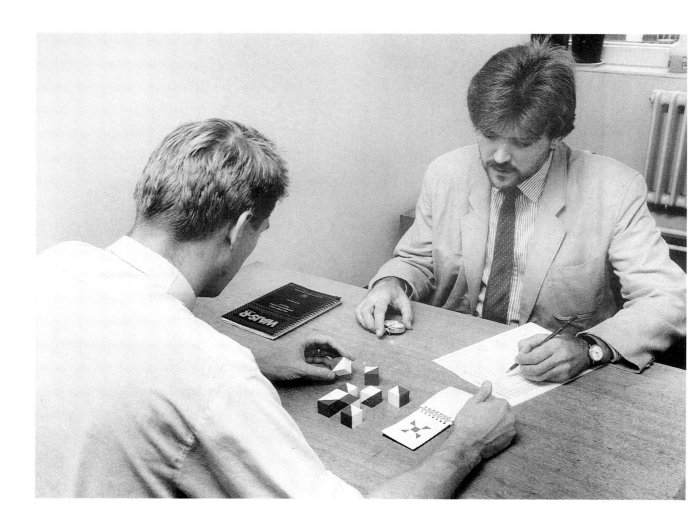

IV 29. Treating disorders of the mind

The philanthropic movement that led to the founding of The London also encouraged thinkers in the eighteenth century to seek how disorders of the mind influenced conduct and behaviour: needless to say, no easy answers were forthcoming. Since then, at different periods in the past two centuries, widely varying schools of thought have determined both medical and general attitudes towards those with mental disorders. For example, one theory which was not therapeutically helpful was that propounded by Dr Hughlings Jackson at The London, who suggested that some mental disorders represented a form of evolutionary regression.

Modern psychiatric medicine has achieved success by adopting open-minded and eclectic approaches and by taking advantage of both medical and psychological methods of treatment. A combination of skills and disciplines is often necessary, including detailed assessment by psychologists and continuing help from specially trained and experienced nurses and psychiatric-social workers. Nowadays many patients are cured and others helped to live with their problems.

IV 30. Care of the spirit

A hospital is a place where matters of life and death impinge upon everyone, whether patients or staff. The role of the hospital chaplains and their colleagues from all creeds is of central importance. They provide comfort and support, sharing in times of happiness and of sadness.

IV 31. Care beyond the hospital

In the early years of the twentieth century the lady almoner interviewed patients to assess their material needs and their ability to pay for treatment if necessary. The department was later renamed the Social Work Department. For 20 years, from 1943, it was headed by Elinor Gough who built it up and established it as an important link with the community. Social workers provide support for patients with economic and emotional problems that often hinder their recovery. They are now employed by the local authority but they remain an integral and necessary part of hospital life.

IV 32. The Marie Celeste Samaritan Society

The Marie Celeste Samaritan Society has now been helping patients for nearly 200 years. Its function is to supply many types of surgical aid and appliance. Here staff are helping a young patient to choose a wig. In addition, substantial grants are made to help with fares for treatment or visiting and with the provision of emergency grants for many purposes. In recent years, the James Hora House has been created on the ground floor of the Alexandra Home for the accommodation of patients undergoing radiotherapy or other treatments, or who have long journeys. Relatives of patients travelling a long distance for very major operations can also stay there.

IV 33. The Friends

Another welcome service is provided by The Friends of The London Hospital. This group aims to make a stay in hospital as pleasant as possible. The Friends raise money to improve amenities for patients and staff; they also organize a team of volunteers to provide services to patients and their relatives. The photograph shows two volunteers with The Friends' trolley; this is very much a part of ward life at The London.

IV 34. The London's many faces

This is an artist's impression of some of the occupations and professions that are represented in the hospital. Many and varied though these are, there are also others not shown here – such as the gardener, the barber, the hairdresser, the radio presenter: the list is endless.

IV 35. Out of the past

The London has a rich history both as a medical institution with a strong tradition of care and teaching and as a part of its local community. This history is manifest in The London's archives – a large and varied collection of volumes, papers, photographs, paintings, drawings and artefacts that trace the administrative, medical and nursing history of the institution. These are stored in the crypt of the former St Augustine-with-St Philip's Church, Stepney Way, part of which has been converted to create a store and study centre. The London appointed its first professional archivist in 1984, when few hospitals saw the need to employ such people; many others are now following suit.

a

b

IV 36. The Information Revolution

The London's board of governors was the first in the country to buy its own computer. This happened in 1964 at the beginning of the 'information revolution'; the application of computers would, in due course, make its mark in every ward and department.

The first machine (now in the Science Museum) was a National Elliott 803 digital computer (*a*). A small space was found for it in the basement of the doctors' residence. Input and output was on paper tape. The computer was programmed in machine code and used

35 mm magnetic film. When working, a sign on it lit up as 'busy'. The multi-disciplinary executive – comprising computing, operational research, administration, medicine and nursing – was to steer The London into the forefront of NHS computing. The advent of the microchip in the seventies led to rapid advances, and the hospital has remained in the forefront of health computing (*b*). Today it has a system that is one of the most sophisticated in the UK, or indeed worldwide.

IV 37. Upheaval in the area: the docks close, Docklands rises

While the computer was quietly revolutionizing life within the hospital, the environment outside was also undergoing great changes. The docks*, for so long a major employer in the area, had declined and in 1981 were finally closed, at which time The London became the area's largest employer. This closure released a vast area of land for redevelopment, now taking place on the doorstep of The London. Buildings once used as warehouses have now become splendid apartment blocks, and city firms have taken up residence in post-modernist buildings, heralding a possible shift in London's commercial centre.

*Reproduced by kind permission of the Museum of London (Port of London Authority Archives).

IV 38. The London Hospital: Mile End and St Clements

No history of The London would be complete without an illustration of its sister hospitals at Mile End (*a*) and Bow (*b*). They too have their own history and Whitechapel is proud to be associated with them.

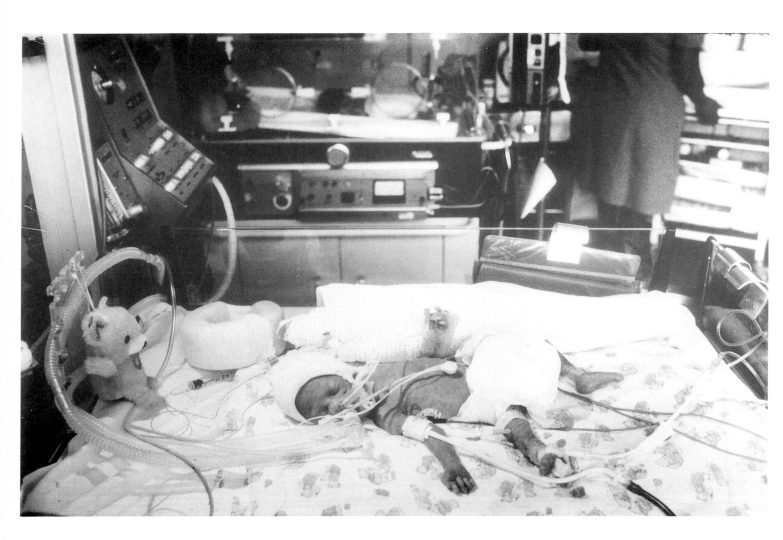

IV 39. The next generation

Ensuring a healthy new generation is as much of a challenge today as it ever was. Advances in this field are truly remarkable: much can be done to assist conception, and to care for and monitor the progress of an individual in the womb. A multi-disciplinary team of midwives, obstetricians and paediatricians ensures that many babies survive and develop normally who would not have done in the past. The continuing care of the child calls for the combined skill and affection of the hospital, community services and the family to combat disease and social deprivation, even in 1990. The baby shown here needs both technology and human care as it joins the next generation.

IV 40. The London: a service to the community

Whitechapel, and the East End in general, have always been places where many races live together. General practitioners in the area, many of whom now practise with their supporting staff from recently built health centres, keep close links with The London and its constituent hospitals. Together they ensure a comprehensive and caring health service for the East Enders of today, whatever their creed or colour.

Further reading

This collection of photographs is intended to introduce the reader to the history of The London and to the development of medicine. It does not aim to be comprehensive, and in the last section in particular, a number of aspects of the work of the hospital have had to be omitted. The authors have drawn heavily upon the archives of the hospital for their material.

The works listed below provide more detailed information on the history of the hospital and some of those who have been associated with it.

BROADLEY, Margaret: *Patients Come First: Nursing at The London between the Two World Wars* (London, 1980)

CLARK-KENNEDY, Archibald: *The London Hospital: A Study in the Voluntary Hospital System.* Two volumes (London, 1963)

—, *Edith Cavell, Patriot* (London, 1968)

—, *London Pride: A History of The London* (London, 1973)

ELLIS, Sir John: *L.H.M.C. 1785–1985: The Story of England's First Medical School* (London, 1986)

GIBBS, Denis D: *Emblems, Tokens and Tickets of The London Hospital and The London Hospital Medical College* (London, 1985)

HOLLAND, Sydney, Viscount Knutsford: *In Black and White* (London, 1926)

LANGTON, Neville: *The Prince of Beggars* (London, 1921)

LÜCKES, Eva: *General Nursing* (9th Edition, London, 1914)

MORRIS, Ernest: *A History of The London Hospital* (London, c. 1920)

RIVETT, Geoffrey: *The Development of the London Hospital System* (London, 1986)

TROMBLEY, Stephen: *Sir Frederick Treves, Extra-ordinary Edwardian* (London, 1989)

Index

Given below are the names of the principal people and places as they appear in the text